The GP Receptionist's Handbook

The GP Receptionist's Handbook

Dr Bennett Quinn

GP Principal
Wallasey
Wirral
UK

Phillip Simons

Research Assistant
Digital Libraries Research Centre
University of Southampton
Southampton
UK

BAILLIÈRE TINDALL
London Philadelphia Toronto Sydney Tokyo

Baillière Tindall
W. B. Saunders

24–28 Oval Road
London NW1 7DX

The Curtis Center
Independence Square West
Philadelphia, PA 19106–3399, USA

Harcourt Brace & Company
55 Horner Avenue
Toronto, Ontario, M8Z 4X6, Canada

Harcourt Brace & Company, Australia
30–52 Smidmore Street
Marrickville
NSW 2204, Australia

Harcourt Brace & Company, Japan
Ichibancho Central Building
22–1 Ichibancho
Chiyoda-ku, Tokyo 102, Japan

A catalogue record for this book is available from the British Library

ISBN 0–7020–1834–1

Typeset by Keystroke, Jacaranda Lodge, Wolverhampton
Printed and bound in Great Britain by WBC, Bridgend, Mid Glam.

Contents

Foreword

Health care is undergoing a time of rapid change. The influence of consumerism and pressure on resources, mean that the role of practice staff is becoming more important. There is a need for them to be equipped with the knowledge and skills to meet the demands of the job. The need is for effective induction into the job and also for ongoing development and training.

Receptionists occupy a unique role between the consumer and the health professionals, and require specific skills. The quality of the receptionist can deeply influence the overall running of the practice. Many problems can be prevented or resolved if the receptionist has the correct tools for the job. These tools include not only the specific skills relating to the job but also an understanding of general administration principles and general practice. These areas are all covered in the book.

This book is a much needed handbook for receptionists and other administrative staff working in primary care. The most difficult time for a receptionist is the first few weeks. There is a lot to learn in a short time. A book like this will go a long way to increase the receptionist's understanding and to maintain their confidence at this crucial stage. The book itself is up to date with health care changes and very practical. It balances knowledge with the skills required for the application of the knowledge. Each chapter encourages participative learning with practical tasks that involve the reader in relating learning to their own practice.

This handbook is very readable and an invaluable reference which I would strongly recommend to all receptionists, whether new or experienced.

Peter Orton
MBBS, FRCGP, MMedSci
Vice-President, Section of General Practice, Royal Society of Medicine

Introduction

- **What this book is for**
  - ☐ This book is intended to be an introduction to the basics of reception work in general practice. It is meant to act as a source of reference and advice to the newly appointed receptionist in the first few weeks and months of work.
  - ☐ In other words, a *survival guide* during those first few months of difficulty that everyone encounters when starting a new job. Quite often a lot of the stresses of a new job occur because the newcomer has such a lot to learn in a short period. This book explains many of the features of the receptionists life, paving the way for further learning and training as you 'grow into' the job.

- **Who this book is for**
  - ☐ Newly appointed reception staff in general practice. If you are in this situation you may find that there is a to lot learn all at once. This book is intended to quickly give you a broad understanding of your new job as a medical receptionist, enhance your self-sufficiency and make you a useful member of the team.
  - ☐ Newly appointed secretarial, clerical and managerial staff in general practice, including those who have not worked in general practice before and who will find this a useful guide and reference.

- **Who might also find this book useful**
  - ☐ Nursing and paramedical staff who are working in general practice and want to understand a little more about the running of their surgery.
  - ☐ GP Trainees or GPs who have just joined a practice as a junior partner.

- **Reading this book**
  - ☐ Don't try to take this book all in at one reading. Instead, the first thing you should do is just browse through the book once or twice so that you know what sort of information it provides, and where.

☐ Don't feel that you have to memorise everything in the book. You can carry out as many of your duties by knowing *where to find* information as you can by knowing facts. So you will use your time more effectively if you get to know the layout of the book rather than all of its contents.

☐ Do get hold of a small notebook and pencil and make constant notes about practice procedures, people and places during your first few weeks in the job. You could use one 'end' of the notebook for people and places details and the other 'end' for procedures. This will save you worrying about committing lots of facts to memory. Instead you will find it a great help to review your notes at the end of every day. But don't forget that there are lots of blank charts included in this book that you will find it useful to fill in and checklists that you can photocopy and refer to, so you don't have to write everything down.

☐ Do take time to look at the various checklists that appear in the book – you can photocopy these if you wish.

☐ Do take the time to do the tasks mentioned in each chapter. There are two reasons for this:

1) doing the tasks makes you *active* in your approach to new knowledge and helps you to take it all in.

2) the tasks help you find out how your own practice does things. This is very important because each practice tends to do things differently and this book can only be the starting point for you to build your knowledge and skills.

☐ If you've been newly appointed this book is ideal for reading or browsing through at home before you start work. You will find Sections I and II extremely useful to read before starting work. They will introduce you to basic concepts and to some of the terminology you will come across in general practice. Once you have read these sections you'll have a background understanding of what is important about your job and why. With this awareness it won't all be entirely new to you when you start work.

☐ Whilst you are at work you can use the book as a handy pocket reference, so don't forget to keep the book with you.

■ **How to approach the tasks**

☐ If you bought this book yourself

it would be good to enlist the co-operation of your practice manager or whoever is responsible for your training *before* you start going through the tasks. You will need the active support of your colleagues with the tasks so they will appreciate you giving them plenty of notice!

☐ If you have been given this book by your practice

then it's fairly certain that they are aware that you will be carrying out various tasks and will support you in this.

☐ When you have completed a task

It's a good idea to make a note of your findings in your notebook.

■ **Features in the book you need to know about**

☐ Each chapter has a brief introduction and a summary at the end so that you can quickly find the information you need. Take time to look at the summary and try to recall the information about each summary point. If you are unsure about a point go back and read the relevant part of the chapter again.

☐ Most chapters have a number of 'tasks'. Please try to take the time for these. These tasks help you to learn by finding information for yourself. You should do the tasks as you come across them in the chapter, but you can leave them until the end of the chapter if you wish.

☐ There are also a number of useful checklists and appendices in most chapters which you may find extremely handy. Some of these are repeated at the end of the book along with a glossary of terms and a list of common abbreviations.

☐ You will find that certain areas of knowledge are repeated in different places in the book. We have written the book this way because the points are important ones and need to be reinforced.

■ **After reading this book**

There are other sources of training and information for developing your skills further as a practice receptionist and for moving on into management tasks. For example:

☐ Training courses provided by the Family Health Services Authority.

☐ Clinical guides and books about medical terminology.

☐ Books and magazines about general practice management.

You can find details about the above in the section on recommended further reading given at the end of this book.

Acknowledgements

We gratefully acknowledge the assistance of Dr Denyse Kershaw and Mrs Jeanette Hooper who painstakingly read the manuscripts. In addition we would like to thank the following: Rosemary Griffin, Steve Marber, Mary Perry and Norma York. We also acknowledge the help and advice from senior managers of Brent and Harrow FHSA.

SECTION I

WORKING IN GENERAL PRACTICE

"HAVE YOU EVER THOUGHT THAT IT MIGHT NOT BE ME WHO'S THE DRAGON!"

|

Description of General Practice

The National Health Service provides access to primary medical care for the entire population of the UK. Since 1948 these services have been mainly free, and available to anyone normally resident in the UK. Qualified and trained GPs are available throughout the country and have become a key part of the health service.

By the end of this chapter you should have a grasp of the following:

1) What a GP is.

2) How GPs are paid

3) The different *types* of practice.

Before you start – Every practice now has to produce a practice leaflet explaining its services for the benefit of its patients. Obtain a copy of your practice leaflet and read it.

THE STATUS OF GPs

The National Health Service provides access to the services of a general practitioner for everybody resident in the UK. There are about 30 000 general practitioners in the UK.

General practitioners are *not* directly employed by anyone; they are *independent contractors*.

Most GPs, besides being qualified doctors, have had two years of specialised hospital training for general practice. In addition they will have spent at least one year working as a trainee GP alongside an experienced GP before joining a practice as a fully qualified GP in their own right.

GPs provide **primary health care** to their patients and are responsible for their care 24 hours per day. This means:

■ Clinical care, i.e. deciding what is wrong with the patient, providing treatment, and/or referring the problem to another doctor.

■ Referring the patient, when necessary, to other specialties such as nursing, physiotherapy, social services, etc.

■ Prevention of illness.

■ Promotion of health.

The designation 'primary' is used because patients will have to see their GP in the first instance when they think they are ill, and distinguishes GPs from hospitals and other specialist services which are called **secondary services**.

Each GP has a list of patients – usually about 1500 to 2500. (The UK average list size is now 1900.) In a city or suburban area most patients will live within about 3 miles of the doctor's surgery. This is so that the doctor can visit patients in their own homes if necessary. In a rural area, some or all of the patients will live further away.

HOW GPs ARE PAID

Instead of drawing a salary, GPs are paid according to a system of fees and allowances.

GPs receive a fixed yearly payment for each patient on their list. This payment is called a **capitation fee**. The capitation fees are paid to the GP for **general medical care** for every patient on their list, *regardless of how much medical care that patient needs*.

See also Chapter 8 where fees are covered in more detail
In addition to the capitation fee, GPs receive **item of service fees**. These are paid for special services that the GP provides from time to time such as vaccinations, maternity care, contraceptive advice, and night visits.

GPs also receive:

■ a basic practice allowance,

■ allowances for their practice premises,

■ allowances for training, and

■ allowances for employing staff in their surgeries.

FAMILY HEALTH SERVICES AUTHORITIES

The organisations responsible for paying GPs are called **Family Health Services Authorities** (FHSAs). (In Scotland these are called **Health Boards** and in Northern Ireland they are called **Health and Social Services Boards**.)

There are about 98 FHSAs in England and Wales, each covering a defined area such as a county or a city borough. In Scotland there are 15 Health Boards, and in Northern Ireland there are 4 Health and Social Services Boards.

The FHSAs maintain lists of patients and GPs in their area and act on behalf of the Government to ensure that each GP is paid the correct amount of money.

FHSAs don't just look after general medical services. They also cover dentists, opticians and pharmacists. They are also responsible for providing information to the public, dealing with complaints and developing practitioner services.

Changes in the NHS mean that from 1 April 1996 the FHSAs will merge with **District Health Authorities**. These are the organisations which purchase secondary health services such as hospital services on behalf of the population of their area. However, even after this change, the FHSA functions of maintaining lists of patients and GPs and making payments will still continue.

DIFFERENT TYPES OF PRACTICE

GPs can organise their practice in different ways:

Single-handed practices

In a single-handed practice the GP works alone, probably in their own surgery with some clerical and nursing support. About 10% of practices in the UK are single-handed. They tend to be either in rural or inner-city areas.

Group practices

A group practice consists of several GPs who share the premises and the workload between them. GPs who are in group practice are usually called 'partners'. Of the practices in the UK, 90% have two or more GPs and 55% have four or more GPs.

Assistants

GPs are allowed (subject to the consent of their FHSA) to employ doctors on a salaried basis to assist them with the patient workload. Such doctors are called Assistants.

Health Centres

In a health centre one or more group practices operate in premises owned by the local health authority. Often there is a wide range of other services available, such as chiropody and social workers.

Rural practices

A **rural practice** can be either a single-handed or a group practice, but the system of payments is slightly different to allow for a scattered population of patients. To qualify as a rural practice at least 20% of the practice's patients must live in a 'Rural Practice Area' *and* at least 3 miles from the main surgery by the normal route. 'Rural Areas' are determined by the local FHSA. (In Scotland, special arrangements for mileage payments may apply for certain Rural practices.)

Dispensing practices

In a **dispensing practice** the GP is entitled to act as a pharmacist and dispense drugs to their patients in return for payments from the Prescription Pricing Authority. Dispensing practices are mostly found in rural areas where pharmacists' shops are few and far between.

Branch surgeries

Practices may also have branch surgeries. These are generally on the fringes of the practice area and may only be staffed for one or two days per week. These allow easy access for local residents.

WHAT GPs DO

GPs are the first point of contact for patients who are ill or who think they have some sort of medical problem for which they need trained help.

GPs either treat the problem themselves or they refer the patient for specialist treatment at a hospital. A patient cannot see an NHS consultant without being referred by his or her GP. The only exception to this is if the patient needs emergency treatment or goes to certain clinics which allow 'open access', a typical example being a genito-urinary clinic. When a patient is treated elsewhere, the GP takes up the care of the patient once the treatment is finished.

Thus the unique points about primary care in the UK are:

- Because the care is continuous, GPs have background knowledge of patients and their families as well as being familiar with the area the patients live in.
- GPs act as a 'gateway' to more specialised and expensive services which cannot be accessed by the patient alone. GPs thus protect hospitals from having to deal with clinically unnecessary work. Similarly, they protect the patient from unnecessary hospital care!
- GPs provide 24 hour cover 7 days a week, including, where necessary, attendance at the patient's home.
- GPs deploy resources for the benefit of the patient and their family. These are not just NHS resources but also services provided by the local authority, social services, and the voluntary sector.

FUNDHOLDING PRACTICES

Under the health service reforms recently introduced some practices have become fundholding practices. Fundholding GPs control the budget for purchasing health care from hospitals and, in some cases, community services.

The difference this makes is that GPs can decide where to spend the budget for the benefit of their patients. For example, they can purchase health care or arrange contracts for care with any hospital, including private hospitals and clinics. They can also purchase health care from alternative medical practitioners such as chiropractors.

If GPs make savings on their budgets they can use these savings to invest in improvements in their practices, such as improved treatment rooms.

Because GPs control funds which previously went to hospitals they can influence the quality of care their patients receive, because if the hospitals and community services don't get patients referred by the fund-holding GPs they don't get the funds. If your practice is a fundholding one you may find that your doctor has arranged for certain activities such as physiotherapy and dietetic clinics to take place in the surgery.

> Ask if your practice is a fundholding one and, if so, how this might affect your work.

CHANGES IN GENERAL PRACTICE

General practice has changed significantly in the last 5 years. GPs now have more influence over how local health services are delivered and far more health-care activity is now taking place at the general practice level.

The best way to keep abreast of all the changes is to try to find time to read some of the magazines that are delivered to your surgery. In particular, *Pulse*, *Financial Pulse*, *GP* and *Doctor* cover the latest developments in a concise and easily readable way.

In this chapter you have learnt:

■ The definition of a GP.

■ How GPs are paid.

■ Different kinds of practice:
  – single handed,
  – group practice,
  – rural practice,
  – dispensing practice,
  – fundholding practice.

2

Key Tasks

In your first few days as a receptionist you will have a lot to learn and you may find it useful to keep your attention on what you are actually there for. The role of the receptionist is to serve the patients and the practice, in that order of priority. This chapter goes into detail about these two main tasks. Frequent reference is made to the more detailed information given in other chapters of this book.

In this chapter you will learn about the receptionists tasks such as:

1) Arranging for the patient to see the doctor or nurse.

2) Arranging home visits.

3) Preparing and managing the consulting session.

4) Managing communications.

5) Closing and locking up the surgery.

INTRODUCTION

Key tasks are the tasks that are necessary to keep the surgery running on a day-to-day basis. In the event of a staff shortage, the practice manager might divert staff from other tasks to ensure that the key tasks are attended to satisfactorily.

Key tasks include the following:

- Preserving the patient's confidentiality.
- Helping patients to see the doctors and nurses.
- Helping patients to arrange for the doctor or nurse to call on them at home (**home visits**).
- Managing requests for urgent medical help.
- Helping patients to order repeat prescriptions.
- Managing communications.

See also Chapter 5 for a discussion on confidentiality

- Preparing for consulting sessions.
- Ensuring that all appropriate forms are signed.
- Updating the practice computer system.
- Filing patient records and correspondence.
- Opening the surgery in the morning and closing it in the evening.

HELPING PATIENTS TO SEE THE DOCTOR OR NURSE

Consulting schedules

Before you start handling requests to see the doctors and nurses you will need some background information on what surgeries (consulting sessions) are available within the practice.

Each doctor and nurse will have his or her own schedule of surgeries. The doctors will generally have two surgeries per day; a morning surgery and an evening surgery.

You will need to know what arrangements have been agreed between the doctors when it comes to seeing each other's patients. Many group practices allow the patients to see any doctor working in the practice. Other practices require patients to see only the doctor with whom they are registered, except in specific situations such as holidays, half-days and emergencies.

As well as routine surgeries, there may also be a variety of other sessions such as special clinics for:

- asthmatic patients,
- diabetic patients,
- maternity care,
- child health surveillance,
- well-woman services, and
- minor surgery.

To complicate the issue still further, the patient may need an appointment to come to some surgeries (**appointment surgeries**) but not others (**non-appointment surgeries**).

If your practice has one or more branch surgeries, the doctor or nurse's working week may be split between the various practice premises.

You may find it useful to take a photocopy of the **Consulting Schedule** form given in Appendix 2a at the end of this chapter for each doctor and nurse working in your practice and to fill it in. You will find this a useful reference when you are trying to remember if a particular doctor is in the surgery on a particular day.

The practice manager will alter the normal schedules when any of the doctors or nurses is on holiday. Surgeries may be cancelled or the practice manager may arrange for locum doctors to see patients. The appointment book will be marked in some way to show the changes.

Find out where the holiday rota for the doctors and nurses is kept and whose job it is to alter the appointment sheets when a doctor or nurse is on holiday.

Making appointments

There are four distinct steps in helping the patient to make an appointment.

Step 1 – Who are you speaking to?

When speaking to patients, either at the reception desk or over the telephone, always make sure you know to whom you are speaking. You should get the patient's name and one other piece of information about them such as their address or their date of birth. If the conversation is over the telephone, you should get their telephone number in case you have to call them back.

When getting a birth date for identification, as long as you have another identifier such as the patient's name, you do not need the full birth date. Just the date and month will do. Thus to avoid possibly embarrassing the patient at the reception desk, you might ask '*When is your birthday?*'.

Step 2 – Who does the patient want to see?

The patient might want to see a particular doctor or they might feel so ill that they do not care who they see.

Sometimes the patient might not be sure who they need to see and you may have to guide them through the services available. This will probably involve discretely asking the patient about the issue. You might say '*May I ask what the problem is?*', or '*To make sure you see the right person it would help me if you gave me some idea of what the problem is'*. When you have some idea of the patient's problem, you will be better placed to help them.

Step 3 – When do they want to see the doctor or nurse?

For less urgent issues and routine reviews, you will work with the patient to find a mutually convenient day and time for the appointment. The patient may have to fit the appointment around other aspects of their life such as work or the care of children or frail relatives.

When offering appointments you should first find a suitable day – *'Would next Tuesday be suitable?'*. Having found a suitable day, you can start to find a mutually convenient time. When a patient says that a particular day or time of day is not suitable they will generally tell you why not. You should use this information when selecting the next appointment to offer the patient.

The consulting schedules for the doctors and nurses may offer different appointment types. The surgery may offer *routine* appointments for general issues, *quick* appointments for simple issues such as the teenager with acute hay fever, and *double* appointments for more complex issues. Sometimes, you might have to make the patient a double appointment with both the doctor and the nurse.

If the patient does not feel very well they will probably want to see a doctor as soon as possible. If there are no available appointments in the next surgery, then this can become a real test of the practice's management and its commitment to looking after its patients. The practice manager should discuss the management of this situation with you. There might be a procedure laid down for you to follow.

Many practices now have **Practice Charters**. These documents will typically state the longest wait for an appointment with *any* doctor (not generally a specific doctor). If the appointment you offer the patient breaks your Practice Charter promise then you may have to refer to a procedure to help you manage the situation, or refer the patient to your manager.

1) Ask your manager how he or she would like you to handle a patient's request for an appointment.

2) If more than one doctor works in the practice, find out if patients are allowed to see a doctor other than the one with whom they are registered.

3) Ask your practice manager what you should do when a patient tells you that they want to be seen *today* and there are no more appointment slots available.

4) Find out if your practice has a charter. Does it contain any reference to how long the patient should have to wait for an appointment?

5) Find out what you should do if you cannot offer a patient an appointment within the charter limits.

Step 4 – Tell the patient when the appointment is

You must make sure the patient knows when the appointment is. This involves accurate message-giving on your part and accurate message-taking on the patient's part. Patients who forget their appointment and then need to make another appointment put an extra load and stress on the appointment schedule. Patients who turn up on the wrong day or at the wrong time also present a problem.

If the patient is at the reception desk you could offer them an appointment card if they do not note the date and time in their diary.

It is more difficult over the telephone. You should speak slowly to allow the caller to write down the appointment time, or you could get them to repeat the time back to you.

Your practice may offer **non-appointment surgeries** where the patients simply arrive before a certain time and are seen in their turn by the doctor. You will just need to tell the patient which doctor is doing the surgery and by what time they need to be in the surgery.

Arranging for the doctor to call (home visits)

The doctor will visit some patients at their home. Patients visited at home tend to be elderly and frail, disabled, or seriously ill. Doctors receive many inappropriate requests for home visits. To make the best use of their time, many doctors have guidelines about the type of cases they are happy to visit at home.

You should obtain the following information:

■ The patient's name, address and telephone number. The telephone number is very useful as the doctor may wish to contact the patient to discuss the problem further.

- The patient's age.

- A brief description of the patient's illness. Some people resent giving this information to a receptionist. You could tell these people that it helps the doctor to plan the order in which they are going to make their home visits.

- Details of why the patient cannot come to the surgery (if this is not already clear from the preceding conversation).

In certain circumstances, which may be defined in a procedure, you may be able to accept the request for a home visit immediately. In other circumstances you may have to refer the request to your manager or to the doctor. You should never refuse to accept a request for a home visit.

You may have to record all telephone calls in a telephone log book.

When a request for a home visit is accepted, you should record the details, usually in a **house calls book**. You should then also get the patient's records out ready for the doctor. If the patient mentioned a recent hospitalisation or out-patient attendance you should check if any correspondence has been received but not yet filed in the patient's record.

1) Ask your manager how you should deal with a request for a home visit. Is there a written procedure for you to follow?

2) What should you do when a request for a home visit has been accepted?

3) Find out what you should do if a caller requesting a home visit declines to give you some description of their illness.

PREPARING FOR CONSULTING SESSIONS

A certain amount of preparation is required to ensure that the consulting sessions run smoothly.

Is the room clean?

Your practice probably has a daily cleaner, but it is always a good idea to take a quick look in the consulting room before the next session begins.

- Does the desk need a quick tidy?
- Does the bin need emptying?
- Does the room smell?
- Is the examination couch clean and tidy?

Is the room adequately stocked?

- Prescription forms.

  Standard **FP-10**s and

  FP10 (MDA)s (HBP(A) in Scotland).

See also
Chapter 10
on Drugs and
Repeat
Prescriptions

If the doctor uses a computer to print out prescriptions, are there enough **FP-10 (Comp)**s and is the printer ribbon adequately inked? Is there a spare ribbon?

- **Med 3**s, **Med 4**s and **Med 5**s.
- Private sick notes.
- Forms to request investigations.
- Syringes, etc., to take samples from patients.
- Headed notepaper and envelopes.
- Examination gloves. These come in various sizes. Make sure you have a selection of gloves to suit the doctors using the room.

See also
Chapter 9 on
medical
certificates
and reports

See also
Chapter 11
on tests and
investigations

Get out the records

This is often called 'pulling' the records.

For a *non-appointment surgery* you will simply get the records out as the patients arrive and deliver them to the doctor. Make sure the records are sorted in order of arrival.

See also
Chapter 5 on
patient
records

For an *appointment surgery* most practices use a box to hold the batch of records required for each consulting session – the *surgery box*.

Some patients may cancel their appointments and the time slot may be taken by another patient. If the records for a surgery have already been pulled, make sure that you update the appointments book and surgery box to reflect the changes.

Make sure that you pull the correct records for each patient. Never depend on just the name. Check two identifiers such as the name and address or the name and date of birth.

Always check that there is somewhere for the doctor to write his or her notes. You may need to add a continuation page.

> When getting out records for a surgery, find out what you should do if there are two patients of the same name at the same address.
> Find out where the stationery cupboard is. Ask what you should do if you notice a dwindling supply of a stock item.

During the consulting session

Updating the appointment list and the surgery box

While the surgery is running, you may have to deal with cancellations and requests for urgent appointments. You have to tell the doctor about these changes in the list of patients he or she has to see and give them the required records.

Receiving patients

The patients will check in with you at the main reception desk as they arrive. You should mark the appointment sheet to confirm that they have arrived.

You will direct most patients to take a seat in the waiting room. Sometimes a patient might complain of not feeling very well or you might spot people who do not look very well. You might direct these patients to a separate room, say an unused consulting room. At the next convenient moment you would then tell the doctor that the patient does not look very well and where they are waiting.

You should always make a point of acknowledging patients as you check them in. Not only does this promote good interpersonal communication but it also gives you a chance to spot people who do not look very well and should perhaps be seen by the doctor as a priority.

Examples of things you might notice at the reception desk include:

– a parent carrying an ill, hot child;
– a patient who is short of breath, and perhaps wheezing;
– a patient who seems to be in a lot of pain.

Find out how the doctor calls patients into the surgery. Do you play any role in this?

Assisting in the further management of the patient

A patient may need an appointment to see the doctor again, or to see the practice nurse for tests or treatment. Alternatively, a patient may have been told that they need some tests done at the hospital, and they may seek your advice on what they have to do next.

Getting forms signed

The doctor may ask the patient to sign some forms before they leave the surgery. It is important that you make sure this is done. This is explained in more detail below.

ENSURING THAT ALL APPROPRIATE FORMS ARE SIGNED

You will read about the FHSA forms that you will meet as a receptionist in Chapter 8. Some forms are also discussed in other chapters.

The income generated by the various forms is crucial to the practice. You must know what the various forms are for and be aware of the situations in which it is appropriate to get them signed.

You must ensure that every form is completed to the practice manager's requirements and passed on to the next stage in their processing.

MANAGING COMMUNICATIONS

The reception office receives information about patients through telephone calls, fax messages, the general post and any **internal post service**. Also, with advancing computer technology, it can only be a matter of time before practices, FHSAs, Health Authorities, hospitals and laboratories are electronically linked via computerised bulletin boards and electronic mail (**email**).

See also
Chapter 11
for a further
discussion of
incoming
information
Your practice will have devised a system to ensure that all incoming information is dealt with in a systematic way. This might be as simple as putting all the letters and fax messages in a tray and giving them to the doctor who will then tell you what action is required.

You will also receive telephone calls from people who wish to speak to one of the doctors. As arrangements for these calls vary considerably from practice to practice, you should ask your manager how you should deal with them. A sample of the possible range of callers is:

- Patients.
- People ringing up to arrange non-NHS medicals such as insurance medicals and HGV licence medicals.
- Other doctors, e.g. other GPs or hospital doctors.
- Hospital secretaries, laboratory technicians.
- Personal calls. The doctors will receive telephone calls from their families and friends. In particular, you should learn to recognise the voices of the doctors' spouses.
- Business calls, 'cold callers' and calls not directly related to patient care. Doctors receive many unsolicited calls from people trying to sell business supplies and services. These calls are probably best diverted to the practice manager.

See also
Chapter 6
where
communica-
tions are
covered in
more detail
You will probably play a role in outgoing communications, e.g. telephoning patients about changed surgery times, faxing urgent messages to consultants and posting the daily post.

1) Find out how you should get messages to the doctor during surgery.
2) Ask your manager how you should deal with telephone calls for the doctor when he or she is in surgery.

UPDATING THE PRACTICE COMPUTER SYSTEM

Information from various sources will need to be fed into the practice's computer system. You may have to key in information from letters received from the hospital, details of vaccinations given, smear tests done, new FP-1001s signed, and test results.

FILING PATIENT RECORDS AND CORRESPONDENCE

All records pulled for the surgeries, repeat prescriptions and home visits have to be re-filed back into the record filing system. All reports and test results that have arrived on any day must also be filed in the patient records. Before this, summary details may have to be recorded on the practice's computer system. Many practices have a policy of trimming letters so that they fit more easily into the record folders.

You must file records and correspondence accurately. If a letter or report is misfiled it might not be found for years. Obtaining copies of lost letters or reports is a major waste of time and money. Always try to match two items of information (**patient identifiers**) before you file a report. Check that the name matches and at least one other item such as the address, the date of birth (best of all) or the hospital case-sheet number.

MANAGING REQUESTS FOR URGENT MEDICAL HELP

This is discussed in Chapter 12 on emergencies.

HELPING PATIENTS TO ORDER REPEAT PRESCRIPTIONS

This is covered in Chapter 10 on drugs and repeat prescriptions.

OPENING THE SURGERY IN THE MORNING

You may have to play a part in opening the surgery premises in the morning. The procedure will vary from surgery to surgery, but commonly the job will include the following:

- Turning off the burglar alarm.
- Removing any security grills from doors or windows used as fire exits.
- Turning on appropriate lighting.

See also
Chapter 6 on
communica-
tions
technology

- Resuming control of incoming telephone calls. You may have to cancel the diversion of your telephone calls or simply turn off a telephone answering machine. If the telephone system has day and night modes, set this to the day mode.

- Set the central heating thermostat to an appropriate level.
- Turn on the computer systems.
- Put the kettle on, especially if it's a cold winter's day.

You will probably learn the opening-up procedure for your surgery by accompanying and observing a more experienced colleague for several mornings.

CLOSING THE SURGERY AT THE END OF THE DAY

Before you are expected to lock up the surgery on your own, you will probably first accompany and observe a more experienced colleague. Like opening the surgery in the morning, the task will vary from practice to practice, but typically you should:

- Make sure that there is no one left in the building.
- Fit the security grills.
- If appropriate, set the telephone system to the night mode. You may then have to turn on a telephone answering machine or set up the diversion of incoming telephone calls to another number.
- Turn off the heating or set the thermostat to a much lower level.
- Go through all the rooms checking that windows are shut and that electrical equipment such as computer terminals, photocopiers and lights are turned off as appropriate.
- Turn off the lights or leave on much reduced lighting.
- Turn on the burglar alarm.
- Make sure you lock the door properly. As a simple security precaution, you should not put the surgery address on the practice keys in case they are lost or stolen.

The tasks of opening and closing the surgery are important.

If, say, the telephone is not transferred, then the night service could be severely disrupted. If security precautions are not followed there could be a break-in, causing disruption to the routine of the practice plus the loss of valuable equipment.

Find out how you would open the surgery in the morning and close it down in the evening. Are there written procedures for you to follow? Ask the practice manager to arrange for you to carry out both an opening and a closing up of the surgery under supervision. This will help you to familiarise yourself with what to do, and where to find things.

In this chapter you have learnt about the role of the receptionist:

- Helping the patient to obtain the most suitable service from the practice.
- Helping the practice to deliver that service.
- Acting as a vital link in communications between patients and practice staff.
- Maintaining accuracy and confidentiality.
- Helping to look after the premises and equipment.

APPENDIX 2a:

(Photocopy at 140% to achieve an A4 form)

Blank consulting schedule

Consulting Schedule for:		
Routine Consulting Sessions		
	Morning	Afternoon
Monday		
Tuesday		
Wednesday		
Thursday		
Friday		

Special Sessions
Ante-natal Clinic
Vaccinations
Child Heath Surveillance
Minor Surgery
Well-woman Clinic

The GP Receptionist's Handbook
ISBN 0–7020–1834–1

Copyright © 1996 B.N.E. Quinn & P.P. Simons
Published by Baillière Tindall Ltd, London

3

People You may Meet in the Practice

In your first few weeks you will meet a number of co-workers in general practice. This can be a bewildering experience, especially if the practice is a large one. However, if you adopt an active approach to getting to know your colleagues you'll soon understand the different skills that each of them brings to the service for the patient, and understand that you all form part of a team caring for patients.

In this chapter you will learn about:

1) The range of staff that you may meet in the surgery, or speak to over the telephone.

2) NHS workers and organisations that are not directly employed by the practice but are in frequent contact with the surgery.

3) Some of the commercial organisations that make contact with the practice.

Don't feel you have to *remember* too much of what you read in this chapter. Instead you may find this chapter useful to refer to during your first few months.

Before you start – arm yourself with paper and pencil and make out blank charts similar to those given in Appendices 3a and 3b at the end of this chapter. Alternatively you may photocopy the charts.

As you work through the chapter you will find it useful to list the grades of staff working in the practice and to record information about them on your chart.

INTRODUCTION

It's important for you to know about the various people who work in the surgery or whose work takes them there occasionally. There are three main reasons why this is important:

1) So you know just *why* different staff are seen around the practice asking for information or assistance. It will raise your confidence level if you know the role that these staff play in the primary health team.

2) By knowing who does what you will gain a good idea of the variety of services offered by your practice.

3) For security reasons you need to know who is allowed behind the reception desk and who is entitled to look at patient's records.

The practice manager will probably introduce you to most of the people you will work with. However, should you see someone to whom you have not been introduced it's a good tactic to take the initiative and introduce yourself as soon as possible. You may find it rather difficult to approach staff who appear remote or busy, but phrases like *'Excuse me, I'm new here, may I introduce myself?'* will help to pave the way.

Find your practice leaflet. Practices are obliged to produce a practice leaflet for their patients. The leaflet should contain:

- Full details of the doctors within the practice.
- The roles of the staff with whom they work.
- Details of the facilities available within the practice.
- The surgeries and the clinics which are provided by the practice.

You can thus make the practice leaflet a useful starting point for finding your way around the practice.

For convenience, the people you may meet have been divided into three categories:

1) People who work in, or visit, the practice.

2) People who work outside the practice.

3) Organisations you may deal with.

PEOPLE WORKING IN THE SURGERY

The doctors

Partners within the practice

A group practice consists of two or more doctors or 'partners' who share the managerial and financial responsibilities for running the practice. Each doctor has the final responsibility for clinical decisions about his or her patients.

The partners have a financial stake in the practice and share any profits between them, in the same way as partners in any other business. However, the responsibility for the day-to-day practice administration may be shared, or be largely in the charge of the longest serving or 'senior' partner. You may find that the senior partner in your practice is approaching retirement and may give the administrative responsibility to a another doctor so that the eventual changeover is smoother.

Assistants

These are qualified doctors like the GPs but are employed directly by the GPs on a salaried basis, often working part-time for just two or three sessions per week. Assistants have the final clinical responsibility for the patients they treat but they have less say in the running of the practice and are not full partners.

Retainer doctors

These are doctors, generally female, who work a much reduced time of up to two sessions per week on a Government sponsored retainer scheme, often while they have family commitments.

Vocational trainees (proposed new title: GP Registrars)

These are fully qualified doctors training to be GPs. They must work for 12 months under the guidance of an approved GP trainer before they can apply to be GPs in their own right.

GP Registrars often have considerable breadth of experience in medical fields other than general practice.

Locums

Locums are doctors who are working temporarily in the practice while one of the permanent doctors is absent from the practice for some reason. The GP remains medically responsible for the service given by a locum to his or her patients.

Ask for a list of doctors working in the practice and fill out your form, using the blank form given in Appendix 3a at the end of this chapter. Don't worry about filling in *all* the items at once. It will probably take quite a while to get all the information.

Shared premises

You may find that your surgery houses more than one group of doctors. In fact in a large health centre there may be two or even three separate practices each with several doctors. If this is the case with your practice you may find that the reception staff for each practice are separate, or that they are shared in some way.

Administrative Staff

Receptionists and clerical staff

Hopefully, when you start work in the practice you will be under the guidance of a longer serving member of staff. You should be clear about who you can turn to when you need help. There may also be receptionists who work slightly different shifts or days to you and who you may never meet. It's a good idea to make contact with them in some way, even if it means dropping into the surgery outside your work hours.

The practice manager

Most practices employ a practice manager who will supervise your work. If it's a small practice, a senior receptionist may have this role. The practice manager is responsible for the smooth running of the practice, and plays a role in the selection of new reception staff members. He or she meets with partners and delivers the ancillary staff viewpoint on current or proposed practice policies and systems. He or she keeps the partnership informed about issues affecting general patient care; for example, if the appointments system is not coping with patient demand. The practice manager also implements partnership decisions and is responsible for staff training or appraisal. The practice manager is the person to whom you refer patient's complaints, when necessary.

Medical secretaries

The practice may have one or more medical secretaries. They are mainly employed to handle correspondence between the GPs and hospitals. For

example, when GPs refer patients to a hospital doctor they write a referral letter to explain the medical problem. The medical secretaries may
also type reports for inclusion in patients' notes.

Business managers and fund managers

If your practice is a fundholding practice you may find that a 'fund
manager' or 'business manager' has been appointed. The fund managers
negotiate contracts for treatment of the GP's patients with service
providers such as hospitals or clinics.

They also look after the practice finances, particularly where a fundholding practice purchases patient care from 'service providers' such as
hospitals.

Computer staff

In a larger practice with many computers there may be a full-time or
part-time member of staff maintaining the computer systems.

Drug dispensers

If your practice is a dispensing practice, then the doctors will probably
employ a dispenser to issue their prescriptions to the patient and to
oversee drug stock management.

Students

You may find that the practice has a number of students from different
disciplines in the NHS. For example, medical, nursing and pharmacy
students may spend short periods in the surgery to find out what goes
on in general practice.

Nursing staff

Practice nurses

Many practices now directly employ a qualified nurse. Such nurses
are usually based in the surgery in a dedicated treatment room. The
practice nurse works under the overall supervision of the GP. The
sort of activities that the practice nurse undertakes depends on their
training, but may include:

- health check-ups for new patients,
- vaccinations,
- childrens' immunisation,
- minor treatments (e.g. syringing ears, doing dressings),

- cervical smears,
- health promotion clinics,
- asthma clinics, and
- diabetes clinics.

The following nursing staff work in close liaison with GPs for the benefit of the patient:

Health visitors

Health visitors are qualified nurses who have a health visitor qualification. Their main areas of work are:

- giving health advice, and

- monitoring the welfare of families, young children and the elderly.

They are usually employed by the district health authority but provide services to patients of the practice. They accomplish this usually by being 'attached' to the practice and are mainly concerned with health education, prevention of illness and advice to parents.

As well as visiting patients in their homes, health visitors may hold or attend various clinics such as well-baby clinics.

A unique point is that patients can refer themselves directly to health visitors – they don't have to go via the GP.

District nurses

District nurses are qualified nurses who have a community nursing qualification.

They are employed by the local health authority or community trust and work mainly in the community, usually carrying out treatments in patients' homes. Usually the patients visited are the chronically ill, the very frail, or those recently discharged from hospital.

The midwife

Midwives are either fully trained nurses who have a midwifery qualification or people who have made a direct entry route into the profession.

They are trained to provide care throughout pregnancy and to provide post-natal care on their own responsibility. Where required they give advice, information and emotional support.

They attend the woman throughout her pregnancy and attend both mother *and* baby after the confinement.

Midwives also carry out examinations at ante-natal clinics and co-operate closely with GPs.

Specialist nurses

Macmillan nurses – These are specialist nurses trained in the care of the terminally ill. The scope of their work includes advice on the general nursing care of the patient, liaising with the general practitioner on medical aspects of care and providing counselling to the patient and the patient's family. They also liaise with the hospital doctors and their colleagues in the local hospice.

Community psychiatric nurses (CPNs) – CPNs give support and counselling to people with mental health problems, and administer drugs where necessary.

Hospital-based nurses who specialise in diabetes, incontinence, or stoma care – These are usually employed in specialist hospital departments, but may be able to offer advice directly to your GP's patients or even run clinics in the practice and visit patients in their homes.

Paramedical staff

The following are likely to be found (mostly working part-time) in a health centre or fundholding practice:

Speech and language therapists

Speech and language therapists (formerly called speech therapists) deal with people who have speech problems; for example, patients with strokes or head injuries.

Occupational therapists

The aim of occupational therapists is to enable patients to reach their maximum level of function and independence in all areas. They assess a patient's disability, advise them on coping with activities of daily living (e.g. teaching stroke patients to dress themselves with one hand) and recommend aids and equipment. If necessary, they can arrange for the installation of aids and adaptations to a patient's home, e.g. fixing extra stair rails and handrails.

Dietitians

Dietitians apply the science of nutrition to a person, both in health and in disease. They provide useful advice for patients suffering from obesity or diabetes, children with dietary problems, and patients who are generally debilitated, say after a major operation.

All dietitians must be State Registered.

Physiotherapists

Physiotherapy is the treatment of a patient's problem using physical methods such as exercise, heat, and electrical and ultrasound stimulation. Physiotherapy is of value in the management of conditions involving muscles, ligaments and bones. It is also useful in helping patients who have suffered a stroke to regain mobility.

Many practices now employ their own part-time physiotherapist.

Chiropodists (now often called 'podiatrists')

Chiropodists deal with problems of the foot, particularly corns, calluses, and ingrowing toe-nails. However, only the following patients can receive free chiropody under the NHS:

- Women over 60 years of age.
- Men over 65 years of age.
- Schoolchildren.
- Pregnant women.
- Registered disabled.

Counsellors

Nowadays more practices are employing counsellors to help patients with personal problems. This is because sometimes people feel they can talk more freely to someone who is not a doctor. Counsellors have more time and are trained to listen to patients and help them to come to terms with their personal problems – but patients have to be referred by their GP.

The benefits of using counsellors can be a reduction in the amount of drugs (such as tranquillisers) taken by a patient and less need for hospital treatment. It also means that patients with minor psychiatric problems have less need to be referred to hospital psychiatric services.

Make a blank chart similar to the one on page 40 of this chapter (or photocopy the chart) and fill in the details of additional staff in your practice.

PEOPLE WORKING OUTSIDE THE PRACTICE

Pharmacists

Pharmacists (more popularly known as 'chemists') dispense the drugs that patients have been prescribed by GPs. There may be several pharmacies that your patients will go to for their prescriptions. You are not allowed to recommend a particular pharmacy, but your practice can keep a list in the reception area for patients to make their own choice.

See also Chapter 10 on Drugs and Repeat Prescriptions

Pharmacists may ring up your surgery if they are having a problem with a prescription issued by one of your doctors.

Other GPs

You may find yourself being contacted by other GPs in the locality, perhaps for social matters or for dealing with on-call and night-duty arrangements.

The police

You may find yourself in contact with the local police on behalf of your GPs regarding the following:

– domestic violence,

– non-accidental injury (NAI) to children,

– security of practice premises,

– difficult or dangerous patients, and

– sudden deaths.

Your GP may also be a **police surgeon**. This means that he or she may be called out from time to time by the police to examine people on their behalf.

The coroner and the coroner's officer

If a patient dies in certain circumstances the GP may need to refer the case to the coroner (the Procurator Fiscal in Scotland) who is responsible for the locality. The patient would usually not have seen a GP in the last 14 days.

This doesn't always result in a 'coroner's inquest' but the coroner needs to be satisfied about the cause of death. Quite often this can be done by making a few simple enquiries. The coroner often has a police officer seconded to his department, called the **coroner's officer**.

The first a GP may hear of a patient's death is when the coroner's officer rings up first thing in the morning. Often the patient may have died abruptly or collapsed suddenly and been taken directly to hospital and died there.

The coroner's officer will discuss the case with the GP. Depending upon the information exchanged and the opinions of both the coroner's officer and the GP the outcome will be that the death either becomes a 'coroners case' or the GP issues a death certificate.

ORGANISATIONS YOU MAY DEAL WITH

Local hospitals

We mentioned in Chapter 1 that you are working in the primary health care part of the NHS. Hospitals are considered the secondary layer of the NHS. You will find yourself in contact with local hospitals for the following reasons:

- Helping to refer patients to a specialist out-patient clinic for an appointment.

- Receiving the results of tests.

- Telephone calls to and from consultants or their secretaries about patients.

- Enquiries about likely dates for a patient's admission.

- Information about a patient's treatment after they have been discharged from hospital.

Ambulance authority

You will have to liaise with the local ambulance control to arrange the transport of patients to hospital, either for admission as in-patients or to attend an out-patients clinic.

The Family Health Services Authority (FHSA)

The FHSA is the NHS organisation that controls GPs and arranges their remuneration. By the time this book is published many FHSAs may have merged with District Health Authorities. However, much of the previous work of the FHSA will still have to be carried on. The sort of issues that may bring you into contact with the FHSA, or its replacement body, are:

■ Checking new patient registrations and de-registrations.

■ Queries about claims for **item of service** fees.

■ Other administrative matters.

Social services/housing

You may be in contact with the local authority about:

■ Fostering and adoption – the GP may be involved in giving medical opinions about the adopters, fosterers and children.

■ Practical advice plus welfare rights.

■ Providing home helps for patients who are not physically able to cope with household chores.

■ Meals on wheels.

■ Respite holidays for people looking after sick relatives.

■ Accommodation for the elderly.

■ Ordinary accommodation – a GP may recommend better housing as a clinical priority for some patients.

One in four practices has a **social worker** attached, so you may meet them in the surgery.

It is vital that all details about patients are kept totally confidential. With many people working in or visiting the surgery, it is very easy for someone to gain unauthorised access to a patient's notes.

■ Find out which of the above people are entitled to look at or modify the patients' notes.

■ Find out what practice facilities can be made available to them, e.g. what offices and equipment they can make use of and if they can use the telephone.

Commercial organisations

Drug company representatives

Drug company representatives often visit the practice to inform GPs about new products, etc.

The attitude of any doctor to the pharmaceutical industry is personal.

> Find out if your practice or individual GPs have a policy about seeing drug reps, i.e.
>
> — never seen,
> — seen only by appointment,
> — only certain companies seen, or
> — open access.

Drug reps may also offer you gifts or other inducements to gain your co-operation in arranging to see the doctor.

> Find out what your practice policy is about accepting gifts or inducements from drug company representatives.

Insurance companies

Insurance companies may write or telephone about reports that they require from the GP about one of their customers.

Solicitors

The GP may be asked for a medical report about one of their patients by solicitors. This generally happens when the patient is involved in legal proceedings.

Support organisations

You will need to be aware of a number of organisations that can offer help and advice to patients. Your practice may have a list of these, but the form given in Appendix 3c at the end of this chapter may help you to create your own.

A FINAL POINT

Make it your business to be aware of who is who around the surgery. This is not only good for work relations but also for practice security. Don't be embarrassed to ask people what their role is in treating patients. You can use your chart-filling activities in this chapter as a way of making contact. True professionals will be delighted to give advice and to explain their work to you.

In this chapter you have learnt about the following people that you may meet in a general practice:

- Doctors:
    - partners,
    - assistants,
    - retained doctors,
    - vocational trainees, and
    - locums.
- Other reception and administrative staff.
- Nurses:
    - practice nurse,
    - health visitor,
    - midwife,
    - district nurse,
    - Macmillan nurse, and
    - community psychiatric nurse (CPN).
- Paramedical staff, including:
    - dietitian,
    - chiropodist, and
    - physiotherapist.
- People outside the surgery:
    - pharmacist, and
    - Other GPs.

APPENDIX 3a:
Practice doctors' details chart

You may photocopy this chart if you wish (To achieve A4 enlarge by 140%).

Details	Doctor 1	Doctor 2	Doctor 3
What they like to be called			
Room number			
Telephone extension			
Pager number			
Mobile phone number			
Home phone number			
List full or open			
Gives contraceptive advice?			
Gives contraceptive advice to under 16s?			
On FHSA Obstetric list?			
On Minor Surgery list?			
On Child Health Surveillance list?			
Takes patients from outside locality?			
Drug reps policy?			
How they like their mail? Who opens it?			

The GP Receptionist's Handbook
ISBN 0–7020–1834–1

Copyright © 1996 B.N.E. Quinn & P.P. Simons
Published by Baillière Tindall Ltd, London

APPENDIX 3a:
Practice doctors' details chart
(Photocopy at 140% to achieve an A4 form)

Details	Doctor 1	Doctor 2	Doctor 3
Afternoon/days off			
On call day(s)			
Tea/coffee preferences?			
Other			

The GP Receptionist's Handbook
ISBN 0–7020–1834–1

APPENDIX 3b:
Other personnels' details chart
You may photocopy this form if you wish (at 140% to achieve A4).

Other practice personnel	Name:	Name:	Name:
Grade/profession			
What they like to be called			
Telephone extension			
Other telephone numbers			
Duties			
Clinics/Sessions			
Allowed to look at patients' notes?			
Allowed to modify patients' notes?			
Other details			

The GP Receptionist's Handbook
ISBN 0–7020–1834–1

Copyright © 1996 B.N.E. Quinn & P.P. Simons
Published by Baillière Tindall Ltd, London

APPENDIX 3c:
Form for listing useful organisations
(Photocopy at 140% to achieve A4 form).

Organisation	Telephone number
Citizens Advice Bureau	
Social Services	
Department of Social Security (Benefits Agency)	
Samaritans	
Drugs Advisory Service	
Relate (Marriage Guidance)	
Cruse (Bereavement Care)	
Other	

The GP Receptionist's Handbook
ISBN 0–7020–1834–1

4

Customer Care

Modern general practice has to take account of the patient's needs just as much as the organisational needs of the practice itself. The rise of consumerism in recent years, the increased level of customer service in the retail sector and Government initiatives such as the Patients' Charter have made patients far more aware of their rights than before. Consequently, their expectations of the service from their GP, and the GP's receptionist, are high.

In this chapter you will learn:

1) Why customer care is important for the patient and for the practice.

2) Some of the techniques of customer care, including listening skills.

3) How to deal with angry patients.

INTRODUCTION

You may never have thought of a doctor's patients as **customers** but the customer philosophy is spreading into most service industries, including medical care. We discuss here the idea of *customer care* and then go on to suggest how you might implement it in dealing with patients.

We don't have customers! Aren't they called patients? Yes, that is true, they are patients. But they are also customers. We are using the word 'customer' in a much wider sense to mean *any* person who deals with *any* other person to resolve a need.

Doctors and their receptionists have been providing customer care with varying degrees of success since the days of Hippocrates. In recent years, however, customer care has been elevated to something akin to a science. While this brings with it the perils of new jargon, it does provide a framework for discussing what is often an ill-defined subject. The general public now has much higher expectations of customer service than previously and is more critically aware of the service they receive from their GP than ever before.

■ Find out if your practice has a customer care policy and, if so, read it carefully.

or

■ Find out if your practice has a practice charter and, if so, read it carefully, noting any standards such as waiting times for appointments.

Patients are the most important customers in every practice. Patients access most of the practice's services through the receptionist. The receptionist *is* the practice in the eyes of the patients. You as a receptionist will often be taken to represent everybody in the practice. For example, a patient may talk to you on the telephone, but they might say later that they telephoned *the practice*. The way you deal with the patient will affect their impression of everyone in the practice. The first few seconds can make or mar that impression. You are 'on stage' whenever the public can hear or see you. This includes talking to staff behind the counter while you are visible to waiting patients.

A receptionist who appreciates the idea of customer care will have fewer difficulties with the patients he or she meets and will probably get more personal fulfilment from the job.

Customer care can be viewed as a tool for several reasons:

■ It makes the patient feel more valued.

■ Customers (*patients*) are important. Without customers, there is no practice. Without the practice, there is no job – not even for the senior partner!

■ Actively seeking to meet the needs of stressed, ill patients probably makes their care easier.

■ It helps the practice to meet higher public expectations and in doing so will reduce the number of dissatisfied customers. Patient complaints arise mostly from a failure of communication. Effective customer care will generally enhance the quality of communication.

■ It can be used as a competitive tool. Patients can take their illnesses elsewhere. Patients can now easily change GP and take their families with them. Or, even if they stay in the practice, they may fail to recommend it to others.

■ It repairs the perceived poor image of the receptionist as a 'dragon'.

Thus, bearing in mind the brief discussion above, how would you implement customer care on a day-to-day basis?

Everyone working in the practice must value the patient and must show the patient that he or she is valued. Every person who comes to the reception desk or who telephones the practice is making your job as a medical receptionist possible. These people are the reason why you have been given a job; you are there to help them.

Doctors' receptionists have the reputation of being 'dragons'. This is not a complimentary image. We suspect that people who call the receptionist at their doctor's surgery a 'dragon' are really saying that they do not feel valued by him or her.

So what do we mean by 'valuing'? You show patients that you value them by:

– welcoming them when they visit or telephone the practice,
– introducing yourself,
– listening attentively to what they have to say,
– acting appropriately to help the patient, and
– guaranteeing that your action will meet the patient's need.

We now deal with these points in more detail.

WELCOMING THE PATIENT

Your welcome might be as simple as a smile or a simple greeting. You should always acknowledge the patient's presence in some way even if you are dealing with something else just at that moment. You might say *'Oh hello, I'll be with you in a moment'*. If you are on the telephone you might nod and smile to acknowledge that you have noted their arrival. If you cannot attend to the patient yourself, perhaps because you are already helping another patient, you should ask one of your colleagues to assist, and tell the patient that you have asked someone else to attend to them. What is important is that the patient should feel *recognized*.

INTRODUCTIONS

You may wear a name badge. If not, you should introduce yourself. You should also make sure that you know to whom you are speaking. As always, you must ensure that you have two identifiers, such as the patient's name and address or, better still, the patient's name and date of birth.

LISTENING TO THE PATIENT

You need to *listen* to the patient to find out what they need. You may need to ask some *open questions* to start the conversation going, such as '*How may I help you?*'.

An open question is one that does not demand a specific answer. Open questions are useful because they get people talking and help you to explore the patient's ideas and expectations. On the other hand, a *closed question* demands a particular reply, such as '*yes*' or '*no*'. You would use a closed question when you have a fairly good idea of the issue under discussion and just want to focus on particular points.

Typical closed questions are:

- Are you registered with this practice?
- Will next Tuesday be convenient?
- Is it urgent?

Closed questions tend to stifle conversation. Sometimes you might get an unexpected reply to a closed question. In this situation you perhaps have a lesser understanding of the situation than you thought you had and should revert to asking open questions.

As a general guideline, you would use open questions to obtain a broad view of the patient's problem and then use closed questions to clear up any points you are not sure about.

Although you obviously have to ask a few questions to get the conversation flowing, you must listen to what the patient has to say, making notes if necessary and interrupting only to clarify points. ***When you are talking, you are not listening!***

To listen carefully, you need to exclude all other distractions such as chatting colleagues and telephone calls. Patients need to feel that they are receiving your full attention. Repeated interruptions will make them feel less valued and may cause them to get irritated.

You should try to make eye contact with the patient from time to time. Many people find this difficult. A useful trick is to look at the bridge of their nose. The psychological result is the same. It is also important to smile when possible.

Leaning slightly towards the patient uses body language to show that they have your attention and that you are listening to what they are saying.

Give occasional listening cues such as '*I see*' or nodding your head, or small mumblings such as '*Uh uh*'.

You may need to slow the patient down, especially when they are stressed. The tactics of making notes as they speak or repeating what they say at a slower rate help to slow things down quite nicely. If you use exactly the patient's own words and phrases it tends to reassure the patient that you are listening to their problems. If the patient is irritated or angry about something, these tactics can also help to take some heat out of the situation.

When the patient has finished explaining their need, you could repeat or summarise the main details to show that you have taken notice of their problem. It is also quite a useful tactic, if the patient is upset or angry, to ask '*Is there anything else you think I should know?*'. This may seem to invite the patient to take up even more time, but it may make them feel they have been allowed to have their say and that you really want to help them.

To find out what the problem is – you have to listen. If you do not know what the problem is, you cannot fix it.

If the patient's problem seems complicated you should perhaps summarise your understanding of the issue back to the patient. When you have understood the problem, you are then in a position to be part of the solution.

ACTING AS REQUIRED

Having identified the problem, the next step is to consider what needs to be done to *fix* it. You should ask yourself '*What can I do to help this person?*'. You should mentally list the options available to you to fix the problem.

After reading this book, and after a few weeks in your job, you will have a clear idea of what options your practice can offer in each situation.

Sometimes it might not be clear how the patient expects you to help them. In these situations it is not unreasonable to ask the patient how they think you can help them. You might say something like '*I see your problem. Tell me how I can help you best*'. This approach may make the patient think more about their problem and perhaps even help them to see how they could resolve the problem themselves. On the other hand, the patient has been thinking about the problem for much longer than you have and may already have an excellent suggestion about how you could probably help them.

When possible, it is always a good idea to involve the patient in the management of the problem by discussing the options with them. The patient will feel more part of the solution and will not feel that something they did not want has been foisted upon them. When the patient feels part of the solution, the solution has a much greater chance of being successful.

Sometimes it will be easy to resolve the problem. On other occasions the solution may not be in your hands – you may have to consult with your practice manager or one of the doctors. If you cannot fix the problem immediately, you should make a commitment to do so within a certain time. When you make such a commitment you should **under-promise, but overdeliver**. For example, the patient's problem may be that they need the doctor to complete part of an insurance claim form. You might tell the patient to collect the form in two days time, but to check with you tomorrow in case it is ready. **Never promise more than you can deliver!**

GUARANTEEING YOUR SOLUTION

You can do this by explaining what you are going to do, for example:

'*Right, I've made that appointment for you*' or

'*I've made a note in the diary to ask Dr Smith to ring you this afternoon*'

'*I will ring the hospital today to find out about your admission date, and ring you back before 5 pm*'

You might simply say '*If there is any problem, just let me know. Ask for me*'.

CUSTOMER CARE ON THE TELEPHONE

When you have to assist a patient or their carer over the telephone, neither you nor the caller can see each other. This means that the body language associated with speech is lost. The smiles, the leaning forward, the relaxed posture, the stressed posture and the eye contact are all missing from the communication. So what you say and how you say it is important.

The basic steps in providing customer care are still the same – welcoming the patient, listening to what they have to say so that you find out their problem, acting appropriately and, finally, guaranteeing your solution. There are, of course, some differences when the conversation takes place across the telephone line.

Good customer care starts the instant you pick up the telephone hand-set to answer the call. You should not be still talking to someone else as you lift the handset. Your practice manager will probably have told you how he or she would like you to answer the telephone. A typical greeting would include the name of the practice, your name and the nice useful open question '*How may I help you?*'.

When taking incoming telephone calls, you must ask the caller to intro-duce himself or herself early in the conversation. If possible, you should then use the caller's name when speaking to them. There are occasions when you would not wish to use the caller's name in order to protect their confidentiality. For example, if you are sitting at the reception desk and you answer the telephone to a young woman asking about her pregnancy test result, you obviously should not say '*Is that Amanda Jones of 9 Upchurch Avenue? . . . Your pregnancy test is positive*'. You might as well have placed a notice in your local newspaper! A better way of han-dling this situation is to obtain enough information from the caller to identify him or her confidently (write it down if you wish) and then use some personal information (such as the patient's date of birth) from the test result as a final check before you release the information.

Although the telephone permits two-way conversation, you may have noticed already how difficult it is to talk into the telephone and listen to what the other party is saying at the same time. This perhaps makes it easier to listen to what the patient is saying. You may find it useful to make some notes. Remember that you need to listen to understand the patient's problem. If you do not understand the problem you are unlikely to be able to do anything about it.

Telephone lines are now generally very clear, but if you have a crackly

See also
Chapter 6
where
telephone
communi-
cation is
covered in
more detail

line or the caller has hearing or speech problems then you may wish to take special care with your communication. You might repeat key phrases, or ask the caller to confirm the message back to you. It would never be good enough to simply *transmit* the message. You must be confident that the caller has *received* it.

> Ask your practice manager if the practice has a standard telephone greeting. If so, make a point of writing it down and keeping it in view for the first few days until you have learnt it.

THE ANGRY CUSTOMER

Some people seem very angry when they come to use the practice's services.

- They might be very worried about themselves or an ill relative.
- They may be under some pressure from a member of their family or their employer.
- They may see you as a barrier to getting to the doctor. Receptionists have a reputation for being 'dragons' and so they may be already in 'angry mode', expecting some kind of confrontation.
- They may feel cross with the practice for some real or imagined wrong.
- They may not remember the usual courtesies if they are ill or in pain.
- They might simply be a difficult person with a poor communication style.

The patient's anger or aggressive approach makes communication hard work and fraught with pitfalls. You should avoid obstructing the patient just because of his or her objectionable affect – that will only make things worse. You should keep to the framework outlined earlier in this chapter, welcoming and listening to the patient, in order to build a working relationship with them so that you can identify the problem, explore how they think you can help them and work with them to fix it.

Another effective technique when dealing with people who are angry and are speaking loudly is simply to avoid adopting a loud tone of voice yourself, and instead speak softly and quietly. The person then has to lower their own voice to listen to you.

Listening is a very useful tool for the angry customer. As well as giving you an outline of their problem, it is also allowing them to blow off some steam. Avoid saying things like '*It's not my fault, I wasn't here yesterday*'. If the practice has let the patient down in some way, do apologise – '*I am sorry that has happened*'. Always show that you have been listening to them by summarising their problem back to them. Then do something about it and guarantee your solution.

You will know you have mastered the art of managing the angry customer when your colleagues compliment you by saying how smoothly you handled the patient.

Many angry customers will leave the surgery smiling and happier. They may have been very worried about themselves or a loved one and are now much relieved that the doctor has reassured them or done some-thing about their illness (and hopefully guaranteed his or her solution!).

Some people just have an awkward communication style. The practice will tolerate these people, perhaps simply accepting them as they are.

IS THERE A LIMIT TO CUSTOMER CARE?

Infrequently, some patients or their relatives will be very objectionable and perhaps even offensive. Exceptionally, you may feel very intimidated or threatened by a patient. These patients may have personality problems or simply be intoxicated with drugs or alcohol.

You should discuss such patients with your practice manager, who may in turn mention it to the doctors. The doctors might explore the issue with the patient, or if there is any suggestion of harm to the well-being of the practice staff or any compromise of the care of other patients they might decide to either ask the patient to register with another doctor or formally ask the FHSA to remove the patient from their List.

You should always report any threat to your practice manager.

OTHER CUSTOMERS

Your customers are not just the patients. Your colleagues in the office, the nurses, the doctors, the health visitors, social workers, the hospital secretaries, the laboratory technicians, insurance companies and solicitors are examples of other customers – i.e. people that you provide a service to.

In your dealings with these other groups of customers you will again find it useful to use the framework of welcoming, introducing yourself (and getting them to introduce themselves to you), listening to what they say, acting appropriately to resolve the problem, and guaranteeing the outcome.

- Find out if your FHSA runs a customer care course. Will the practice manager want you to go on it?

- The doctors may sign your monthly cheque, but ... who really pays your wages?

- Next time you are a customer, e.g. when visiting your corner shop, paying your gas bill, visiting the dentist or dealing with the bank, observe how you are dealt with:

  – Do you feel valued?

  – Are they interested in your business?

  – Do you get uninterrupted attention?

  – Does their service meet your needs?

  – Will you use their service again?

  – Would you recommend them to your friends?

Discuss the following scenarios with your practice manager:

1) *You answer the telephone. A man tells you that he picked up his repeat prescription an hour ago and that his stomach pills have been omitted. This is the third time this has happened. He sounds distinctly irritated. What are you going to do?*

2) *It is a busy morning. Three doctors and two nurses are consulting. The waiting room is packed. A young man comes in. He seems unsteady on his feet. He tells you he does not have a local doctor, that he is ill and needs to see a doctor. He will not be drawn on the nature of his illness. As he is talking you notice that his speech is slurred.*

You find that all appointments for the day are fully booked and suggest an appointment for the next day. He becomes very agitated and starts shouting loudly in very abusive terms that he needs to see a doctor. He nearly knocks over one of your elderly patients.

Everyone in the waiting room is looking at you and this young man. What are you going to do?

In this chapter you have learnt:

■ The importance of customer care.

■ Some ways you can make the customer feel valued:

  − recognition,

  − listening, and

  − guaranteeing your action.

■ A few hints about dealing with angry or dissatisfied customers.

■ A few points about dealing with patients on the telephone

■ That your colleagues both inside and outside the surgery are also customers.

GENERAL ADMINISTRATION

The Patient Record

A patient's record represents the entire primary health medical history of that patient. It is therefore a central point of reference for the GPs and their staff. As the patient moves around the country and from GP to GP their record 'travels' with them, thus providing continuity of medical care throughout the patient's lifetime.

Loss or misuse of a patient's records could cause serious damage to the health care of that patient.

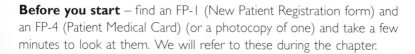

In this chapter you will learn:

1) How the patient joins, and leaves, the doctor's list.

2) Procedures involving patient records, particularly when patients join and leave the practice list.

3) Features of, and problems with, patient records, including computerised records.

4) The importance of confidentiality of patient information.

Before you start – find an FP-1 (New Patient Registration form) and an FP-4 (Patient Medical Card) (or a photocopy of one) and take a few minutes to look at them. We will refer to these during the chapter.

INTRODUCTION

Your practice will have a record file for each registered patient. These record files (**FP-5** for men; **FP-6** for women) (in Scotland, GP5 and GP6; in Northern Ireland, HS 123) contain notes made by the doctor and nurses when they see the patient, and letters, reports and other correspondence received about that patient.

One of the great merits of general practice is that the patient's record is transferred from GP to GP as the patient moves from area to area, or even from practice to practice within a particular area. This means that continuity of the patient's care is made easier as details of their important previous medical health follow them through their life.

As well as the normal manual or paper-based records, many practices now also have computers that they use to help with patient management. A very basic computer function is to keep a track of who is on the practice's list.

In this chapter we explain first what happens to patients' records as they join and leave your practice, and the various procedures involved. Next we discuss the features of the record itself, including computerised records and records for temporary residents, and then go into some of the problems that can arise with patient records. Lastly, we discuss the vital topic of confidentiality.

THE MANAGEMENT OF PATIENT RECORDS

We are now going to look at the various steps in the management of the patient's records:

- How a patient joins the practice list.
- How the practice gets the patient's record.
- How the practice might process the newly received patient's record.
- How the patient may be removed from the doctor's list.
- What needs to be done before a patient's records are returned to the FHSA.

How does the patient join the list?

The list of patients registered with a practice is often simply called the **list**. When a patient registers with the Practice, they are said to **join the list**. When the patient leaves the practice, they are said to **offlist**. People may apply to join your doctor's list for a variety of reasons. They may have just moved to the area, be discontented with their present doctor, or may have heard wonderful things about your practice. Exceptionally, patients can be allocated to your doctor's list by the FHSA.

The prospective patient's approach to the practice must be managed carefully. You should ensure that you meet their needs by listening to what they have to say and addressing any questions they raise. You must also consider the needs of the practice. All practices now have practice information leaflets and many have practice charters. All new patients, expect those allocated by the FHSA, must sign either form FP-4 or form FP-1. Often, the patient should also sign other forms, such as the FP-1001 (Contraceptive Services) or the FP-24 (Maternity Services). These two forms will be discussed in detail in later chapters. The practice may have a written procedure, or protocol, for you to follow when you register a new patient. An example of such a *new patient protocol* is given in Appendix 5a at the end of this chapter. These protocols may include asking the patient to complete a questionnaire about their previous medical history and current drug prescriptions. Many practices bundle all these leaflets, forms, questionnaires and protocols into *new patient packs*.

Ask your practice manager how he or she wishes you to process the prospective new patient.

Doctors will generally only accept applications to join their list from people living in their **practice area**. The doctors define their practice area. You should not normally accept patients who live outside the practice area. The practice area may simply comprise a list of district names or may be defined by lines drawn on a map. Sizes of practice areas vary enormously. A city practice will typically have a much smaller practice area than will a practice in a small country town.

Find out what your practice area is. Can you easily check if a patient lives within the practice area? Ask your practice manager how strictly should you adhere to the practice area. For example:

1) A family of four who live 100 yards outside the practice area wish to join the list. What should you say?

> **2)** Mr and Mrs Exmouth have been with the practice for over 20 years. Their children are all grown up and they have moved to a smaller house in a district just outside the practice area. What do you say to them when they give you their change of address?

Before you send the FP-1 or FP-4 to the Family Health Services Authority (FHSA) some initial processing probably takes place.

Some of the things the practice might do at this point are:

- *Simply record the new patient's details in a register.* Like any other piece of paper, an FP-1 can go astray. It is wise to have some system to cross-check new patient applications against FHSA confirmations. A simple system would be to record the new patient's details in a register or ledger.

- *Add the new patient to the computer.* Computerised practices would probably then add the patient's details to their computer. The new computer entry might be marked in some way showing that registration has not yet been confirmed.

- *Make out an index card for the new patient.* Many practices keep a card index of all their patients, but this is less common now with the widespread use of computers. If your practice has a card index you should make out a card for the new patient.

- *Create a temporary record file for the patient.* This is useful as it will take several weeks before you receive the patient's previous record. During this time, the patient may require medical attention or repeat prescriptions. You will need somewhere to record these events.

> Find out what happens to the FP-1 or FP-4 in your practice before it is sent to the FHSA.

> Ask your practice manager how medical records are processed when they arrive in the practice.

How does the practice get the patient's record?

When you have processed the FP-1 or FP-4 to your practice's requirements, you should send it to the FHSA to have the patient included (**registered**) on the doctor's list. If the patient is not registered, the practice will not receive any income for him or her. You can see that this would be a very unsatisfactory state of affairs.

The FHSA will confirm the patient's registration on form Z68. They will then request the patient's record from the previous doctor. Where the previous doctor is with another FHSA, the request goes to the other FHSA who then obtains the records from the GP and forwards them to your FHSA. This transfer of records takes time.

For urgent cases, or for patients with complicated medical problems requiring ongoing management, the practice can contact the previous doctor directly to request the notes. Most doctors receiving such a request would forward the notes to the new doctor, probably by registered post, keeping only the actual record envelope. The empty record envelope is then sent through the normal record transfer system with a clear message that the notes have been sent directly to the new doctor.

Another method of getting records urgently is to ask your FHSA to obtain them for you. FHSAs now have *quality statements* that may include providing urgently required records within a specific period.

You need to find out what happens to the records when they arrive at your practice. Some practices might simply file them with all the other records. However, to do so would miss a valuable opportunity to obtain information that affects clinical management or practice income.

The notes may contain details of an important condition that requires periodic review, such as an underactive thyroid gland. Other conditions may require urgent action, such as an abnormal cervical smear test result. Current Government policy is to set targets for vaccinations, cervical cytology, health promotion and chronic disease management. The records will probably contain information that will help the practice in its management of the various targets.

Some ideas for the management of newly received medical records are:

Record the safe arrival of the notes – the practice manager probably has some system to record their safe arrival. Several steps might be required such as noting the date of receipt in the same register used to record the FP-1s and altering a computer record.

Sorting the record – the letters may not be filed in an order preferred by your practice.

Trimming the correspondence – letters and reports tend to have large areas of white space, i.e. paper with nothing or nothing important written on it. Trimming letters and reports of their white space makes them easier to file and makes the record less bulky. You should make sure that vital details such as the letter date, the name of the author and the patient's hospital record number are still on the trimmed letter.

Pruning the record – records can contain multiple copies of the same letter and multiple letters about single episodes of illness. It is often possible to prune some of this excess correspondence from the notes. This task ought to be done by one of the practice's nurses or doctors.

Summarise the important medical history – many practices summarise important medical history on a separate sheet in the medical record or on the practice computer. This greatly assists clinical management by allowing the doctors and nurses to focus quickly on the patient's past history.

From an administrative point of view, it is currently important to identify patients suffering form asthma or diabetes, as these patients are the subject of separate health promotion activities.

Clerical staff could check records for certain diagnoses such as thyroid trouble, epilepsy, asthma and diabetes. These conditions are easily identified by the drugs a patient is taking.

For a comprehensive summary of the past history, a doctor or a nurse would have to examine the records.

See also
Chapter 13
on
vaccinations

Check vaccination records for children aged under 6 years – it is very useful to go through the records of children aged under 6 years, and note what vaccinations they have had. Prompt identification of a child who has not yet had all the required vaccinations might save the practice from missing a valuable target payment. An unvaccinated new child patient might lower the practice's vaccination achievement by 1–5%, which might be significant if the practice is only just achieving a particular target level.

Children overdue for their vaccinations might be 'picked up' before the FP-1 or FP-4 is sent to the FHSA by using a pre-registration screening process such as an interview or a questionnaire.

Check for recent cervical smear tests – Women aged between *25 and 65* years form the cervical cytology target group. You should check the records of women in this age group for details of any smears done during the previous 5 years. You should record the details on whatever system, computerised or manual, the practice uses to manage its cervical cytology workload.

See also Chapter 14, where cervical cytology is covered in more detail

- *Were the recent smears normal?* You should look at the results of the more recent smear tests. If any results were abnormal you should draw this to the attention of one of the doctors.

- *Has the patient had a hysterectomy?* Patients who have undergone a total hysterectomy are excluded from the target group. Having found a reference that possibly suggests that the patient has had a hysterectomy you should ask one of the practice nurses or doctors to confirm it for you. This is so that you do not erroneously cancel the patient's smear recall. You should then make sure this fact is recorded appropriately and the FHSA *notified* so that the patient may be excluded from the target group.

As the target group for cervical cytology is generally quite large, it would not often prejudice a target payment if a new patient was overdue for her smear.

Should the patient sign form FP-1001? – You should check if a female patient was receiving contraceptive services from her previous doctor. If so, then you should ensure that the patient joins the practice's contraceptive list, using form FP-1001 if she has not done so already. This form should be signed at the earliest possible moment to maximise practice income – up to 9 month's (three-quarters) extra payment might be gained. Again, a pre-registration interview or questionnaire can be useful here.

See Chapter 14 where form FP-1001 is covered in more detail

Record any health promotion activity – for patients aged between 15 and 75 years any record of health promotion activity should be logged on your practice's system for recording this information. This helps the practice to maintain any target achievement. The health promotion target group will be large and so the lack of health promotion detail will not greatly upset any target achievement.

Transfer temporary notes – any temporary notes made while waiting for the full records should now be joined up with them.

Ask your practice manager to show you a recently received Z68 and to explain to you how it is processed within the practice.

How does a patient leave the list?

Patients can be removed from the practice's list for several reasons. The FHSA uses **form FP-22** to tell the practice about offlisted patients and to request return of the records. Some processing is required before the records are returned, although this should be done as quickly as possible as the doctor could be in breach of his contract if there is an unacceptable delay.

Let us look now at the methods by which a patient might be removed from the practice's list.

The patient joins another practice

Patients have the right to change their doctor. This is an obvious necessity when they move out of your practice area. Sometimes patients may move to another doctor if they have had problems with your practice or if another practice is offering a better service. Patients do not have to tell you if they are leaving your list and neither do they have to tell you why they are leaving your list. Some patients may pop in to thank you for looking after them.

When the patient signs an **FP-1** or **FP-4** at the new practice, it is forwarded to the FHSA who will then remove the patient from your list.

The patient dies

The Registrar of Births and Deaths notifies the FHSA of all deaths. The FHSA will then remove the deceased patient from the practice's list.

Form FP-69

If a letter sent by the FHSA to a patient is returned through the Post Office's Dead Letter Office, or is returned indicating that they have moved away, or the patient does not respond despite a reminder, then the FHSA will remove the patient from the list 6 months later unless the practice can confirm that they are providing general medical services to the patient. Some action is required to make sure that the FHSA does not remove a patient from your list who perhaps simply did not respond to a standard mailing and who may use the practice's services at some point in the future. The FHSA might not have the correct address for the patient if, say, the practice failed to inform them that the patient had moved.

The FHSA will send the practice a form FP-69 with the patient's name and registered address on it. You should check if the FHSA's registered address for the patient matches your records. If not, then you have found a likely explanation for the problem. You should fill in the correct address in the appropriate space, get the form signed by the doctor if he is prepared to keep the patient on the list and return it promptly to the FHSA.

If you have a telephone number you could try to contact the patient. Alternatively, you could send them a letter asking them to contact the practice. Obviously, if you make contact with the patient you will probably resolve the problem.

If you cannot make contact with the patient, and the FHSA's address matches your records, then the FHSA may have found one of your **ghost patients** (a discussion on 'ghosts' follows later in this chapter). You should file the FP-69 in the patient's record and mark the patient as a ghost on whatever system is in use in the practice. If the patient presents during the 6 months then you should find out their current address and decide if the patient can stay on the list. Form FP-69 should be completed appropriately and returned to the FHSA.

The doctor asks the FHSA to remove the patient from the list

The doctor is entitled to have any patient removed from their list. This might happen if the patient has moved outside the practice area or if there has been an irretrievable breakdown in the relationship with the patient. Patients might also be removed from the list if their behaviour is unacceptable, e.g. because of violent or abusive behaviour towards the reception staff or if they are placing unacceptable and inappropriate demands upon the practice. Patients who, say, frequently demand home visits for trivial or minor issues, frustrate the doctors and, by taking up the doctor's time, compromise the care of other more needy patients.

To offlist a patient, the doctor simply writes to the FHSA requesting their removal. The FHSA will confirm that the patient is to be offlisted. The doctor is responsible for the patient's medical care for a further 14 days unless they find another doctor in the meantime.

Processing form FP-22

The FHSA usually notifies the practice about offlisted patients in batches so that each FP-22 may have details of more than one offlisted patient. Before the practice returns the manual record some administrative steps are required:

■ You should check that the patient has not been seen after the date of offlisting as shown on the FP-22. If they have, this might suggest that a mistake has been made, or that an FP-19 or FP-106 (discussed in more detail in the Forms chapter) should be signed.

■ You should include in the manual record a printout of whatever is stored on the practice computer about the patient.

■ You should note on all manual and computerised systems the fact that the patient has left the list. It is important to have some way of knowing if a patient has left the list so that you can resolve any subsequent enquiry.

See also Apendix 15a for a discussion of form FP-24

■ For female patients you should check if there is any outstanding claim for maternity services (**FP-24**) and ensure that these are sent off for payment. If the patient offlists before her post-natal examination you should ensure that the date of last service is recorded on the form.

Remember that if a doctor is unreasonably slow in returning records when requested by the FHSA he can be accused of breaching his or her contract.

Ask your practice manager to show you an FP-22 and to explain to you how it is processed within the practice.

If the practice's registration under the Data Protection Act shows that it intends to store records on previous patients, then the patient's computer records do not have to be erased. Computer systems may retain details of the patient for some considerable time. If the patient rejoins the list, their details might still be available. This is obviously useful. This feature makes the computer a useful tool for quickly checking a patient's registration status.

FEATURES OF THE PATIENT RECORD

Paper-based records

Record storage and retrieval

There are two main types of folder or envelope in use for patient records:

- The Lloyd-George medical record envelope.
- A4 size record folders.

The **Lloyd George medical record envelope** is the most common storage format. Their compact size has merits but is also one of their greatest drawbacks. They soon swell up with doctors' notes and hospital reports. Many practices have a policy of trimming all correspondence as it arrives in the practice, thus reducing the bulkiness of records. Similarly, many go through records at intervals to summarise important events in the patient's medical history and to prune correspondence from the file.

Some practices use **A4 record folders** (8.27" wide by 11.69" high). These offer advantages over the Lloyd George envelope in that correspondence can be filed without trimming or folding. However, A4 notes present a problem if the patient moves to another doctor who uses the more common Lloyd George records – the A4 notes make the small Lloyd George envelopes very bulky.

The cover of the record folder shows:

- The patient's surname and forename.
- Their date of birth and National Health Service Number.
- The patient's sex.
- Several boxes for the patient's address and the doctor's name. The patient's current address is the last one in the list. The patient's current doctor is the last one in the list. The FHSA stamp against each doctor's name shows the date on which the patient was registered on their list.

Inside the record folder you will find:

- Handwritten notes made by the various doctors and nurses who have looked after the patient during his or her life. Administrative details might also be recorded in the notes. For example, if a patient's FP-1001 (claim for contraceptive services) is due, it might be practice policy to write this prominently in the notes.
- Letters and reports, hopefully sorted by date, from the various

See also Chapter 14 where form FP-1001 is covered in more detail specialists whom the patient has seen over the years.

■   Laboratory and x-ray reports.

■   Some practices also use special sheets to record information about specific areas, such as contraceptive services, maternity care, repeat prescriptions, or important past medical history. These sheets will also be kept in the patient's record.

A schedule of commonly used record stationery is given in Appendix 5b at the end of this chapter.

Your practice will have many records to look after, 1800 to 2000 per full-time doctor on average, and will have set up a filing system to simplify easy storage and retrieval of records when required. The records will almost certainly be filed alphabetically. Some practices separate men's and women's records. Others keep notes for all members of a family together in larger envelopes. You should familiarise yourself with the system in use in your practice.

Patients with similar names are a major problem. A basic step is to put a warning sticker on the front of the notes warning that there is another patient with a similar name. This also underlines the importance of never simply using a name for patient record retrieval. Where possible, you must use some additional item of information. An address is perhaps the most commonly available second piece of information and is certainly useful. The best additional piece of information is the patient's date of birth. The chances of two patients having a similar name and the same date of birth are small.

Records for temporary resident patients

A temporary resident (TR) is a patient who intends to stay in your practice area for less than three months.

You should make sure that each TR has signed an FP-19 (in Scotland, GP 19; in Northern Ireland, HS 15) and that the FP-19 is still current. The back of this form is intended for clinical notes. Practices generally keep these forms separate from their normal records. If a TR requires further notes then you could use the usual continuation sheets (FP-7 for men and FP-8 for women). Treasury tags or staples can be used to keep the separate sheets together. When the TR returns home the notes should be forwarded to the FHSA who will then send them to the patient's GP.

Computerised records

> Practices using computer systems to process patient related information must be registered under the Data Protection Act. This Act provides an avenue for patients to inspect their computer records (on payment of a fee). The Data Protection Registrar can prosecute computer users that fail to meet the Act's requirements for accuracy and confidentiality.

The computer program generally allows the user to find an individual patient's record and to enter new details about the patient. You can print out these details when required.

Computer systems go much further than simply accessing individual patient's records however. You can use them to find groups of patients who have something in common such as particular medical conditions or those receiving particular drugs. They are excellent for targeting groups such as women overdue for their cervical smear and writing letters to them.

You will need training on how to use the computer system. You will need to be assigned a password. Your assigned password will be intended to be temporary and you should change it when possible to one known only to yourself.

See also Chapter 7 where computers are discussed in more detail

PROBLEMS WITH PATIENT RECORDS

Missing records

From time to time, records go missing. The practice may have a search procedure, which probably includes the following steps.

■ Checking for misfiling, e.g. look in the men's records for a missing woman's record.

■ Check if the records have been taken out because the patient has requested a repeat prescription.

- Check with the medical secretary who may have the record for processing a referral to a specialist.

- Check if a doctor has the record for some reason, e.g. an insurance enquiry or a medico-legal report.

- Many people are not known by their legal name. For example, Edward Jones may call himself Ted Jones and Mary Isobel Smyth may call herself Isobel Smyth. The practice computer may help to resolve this problem.

- Is the patient a young woman who may have changed both her surname and address when she recently married?

- Check if the patient is actually on the list:
  - Are they a temporary resident?
  - Have they telephoned the wrong doctor?
  - Have they left the list?

For example, a young patient might have left your list when they went to college but may seek medical attention when they are home during holidays. Their request for an appointment may trigger consternation when their record cannot be found. Referral to a log of offlisted patients will quickly show that you need to get an FP-19 or an FP-1 signed.

Where necessary, you should confirm with the patient that they are registered when they present for the appointment.

- A child's surname may be different from that of their parent. A mother might ring up to make an appointment for her child and erroneously give her own surname as the child's. You could use the practice's computer to find patients living at the address given by the mother when she made the appointment.

If you cannot find the record in time for the surgery consultation or house call, you should make up a temporary record. A temporary record will often comprise little more than a continuation sheet with the patient's name, address and date of birth. Remember to associate the temporary record with the full record when it does eventually come to hand.

Ask your practice manager what you should do when you cannot find a record, and how you should make up a temporary file.

Changes of name or address

It is important that the practice knows exactly where its patients live. The doctor may wish to call upon the patient for some reason and will depend on the practice's information systems to give him or her the correct address. On a larger scale, the distribution of the practice's patients around the locality may influence management decisions, such as whether or not to open a branch surgery. Inaccurate recording of patients' addresses may undermine such decision-making. Whenever you become aware that a patient has changed their surname or moved house there are several important things you must do.

■ You must establish who the patient is, their old address and their new address or new name. You should get their new post code and telephone number.

■ You should ask if any other patients have also moved and, if so, make a note of their names.

■ If the patient has moved outside the practice area, then you should check with your office manager or the doctor if the patient can stay on the practice's list. If you accept a change of address to somewhere outside the practice area you put the doctors at risk of having to do home visits to that address. An out of area home visit would take up an unacceptable amount of the doctor's time. A doctor might do two or three more local home visits or see six to eight patients in the surgery during the same time.

If the patient's new address is acceptable to the practice, you should then make sure that the change is recorded on the patient's notes and all other information systems used by the practice such as the computer and the index card system.

You must make sure that the FHSA is told about the change of name or address. The FHSA may provide a form for this purpose. Some computer systems can generate a list of changed names and addresses for the FHSA.

Find out what you should do when a patient tells you that they have changed their name or address.

Ghost patients

When you lose track of where a patient lives, they become a 'ghost' patient. The patient may have emigrated, may have died away from home or may have inexplicably become lost to the system.

You will find 'ghosts' when letters are returned as undeliverable. You could also use the practice's computer to find potential 'ghosts' by asking for a list of patients who have not been seen for a long time (at least 3 years).

See Chapter 13 for details of target payments

'Ghosts' have their good points – they don't bother the doctor and they earn the practice money in capitation fees. They have their bad points too – they distort practice planning and they count towards targets.

'Ghosts' do not get vaccinations or cervical smears done and they don't present themselves for health promotion activities. A sizeable 'ghost' population may make the difference between a low target payment and a high target payment.

The practice may have some way of logging 'ghosts', perhaps using a register or perhaps using the practice computer. A practice achieving fractionally less than the higher cervical cytology target will be very keen to identify quickly any female 'ghosts' aged between 25 and 65 years.

Before removing 'ghosts' from the list, the practice might write to each one asking them to contact the practice. Some 'ghosts' will turn out to be just very healthy people who have not had to see a doctor for years.

Find out how you can check that a patient is registered.

PROTECTING PATIENT CONFIDENTIALITY

The practice has a duty to protect the privacy of its patients. The consequences of any breach of a patient's confidentiality could be severe. Apart from any anger or embarrassment suffered by the patient, leaks of certain types of information could compromise the patient's marriage or job. An accusation of a breach of confidentiality would be a major problem for the practice. The resulting bad publicity would damage the practice's reputation. The doctor is the person who would be held responsible for any breach of confidentiality. The fallout for the doctor might include being sued for damages, being reported to the General Medical Council, and being prosecuted under the Data Protection Act if the breach was related to computer data. Any employee of the practice who breached or compromised patient confidentiality would be subject to disciplinary action. It would be a serious matter, possibly resulting in a written warning or perhaps even dismissal.

You may know many of the practice's patients. Indeed, you may even have been to school with some of them. They may be members of your social club or simply frequent the same hostelry. You must be especially careful not to breach a patient's confidentiality when you are socialising outside the practice.

It is technically a breach of confidentially to even admit that any particular individual is a patient of the practice.

Common situations where confidentiality can be easily compromised include:

- Talking about a patient within earshot of others, e.g. other patients sitting in the waiting room.
- Talking to the patient at the reception desk or on the telephone, again within earshot of others in the waiting room.
- Volunteering to a patient that there is a prescription waiting for another family member or that another family member saw the doctor yesterday. For example, you might give a parent their daughter's prescription for the contraceptive pill or you might tell a patient that their spouse saw the doctor yesterday only to find out that they did not know about it!

The practice must also protect the patient's medical records. You should make sure that a record does not fall into the hands of someone who is not entitled to have it. For example, you should not leave records or patient related notes near the reception desk where some unscrupulous person might take them. Remember that people waiting at the reception desk can read writing upside down.

You should know who is entitled to read patients' records. You should find out if the various other professionals working with your doctors are permitted to read patient records. You yourself must be professional when accessing patient records. Checking up what medicines a patient receives so that you can prepare a repeat prescription is legitimate. Using your position to check if an acquaintance has had her new baby yet or whether your neighbour's teenage daughter is really on the contraceptive pill would not be legitimate and would leave you open to criticism.

See Chapter 7 for more details about passwords

Computer records are generally protected by passwords. Your password gives you access to certain programs and certain information. Your access may be increased as you are trained to use the computer or as you gain seniority in the practice. You should guard your password because it is vital to keep patients' records confidential.

In this chapter you have learnt:

- The purpose of the medical record.
- How the practice obtains a patient's record.
- Procedures and problems with patients records, such as:
  - dealing with newly arrived records,
  - missing records,
  - sorting and trimming records,
  - when a patient changes address, and
  - when a patient leaves the GP's list.
- The importance of confidentiality in all aspects of patient care.

APPENDIX 5a:

An example of a new patient protocol

(Photocopy at 140% to achieve an A4 form)

Name	
Sex	Male/Female
Date of Birth	—— / —— / ——
Maiden Name	
Address	
Post Code	
Telephone numbers	Home Work
Does the patient have to see one of the doctors before they can be accepted to the list?	Yes/No
FP-1 or FP-4 signed	Yes/No
Appointment made for new patient medical?	Yes/No
Women: Will they require contraceptive services? If YES, FP-1001 signed?	Yes/No Yes/No
Women: Are they pregnant or have they had a child within the last three months? If YES, FP-24 signed?	Yes/No Yes/No
(Children aged less than five years and practice offers child health surveillance) FP/CHS signed?	Yes/No

The GP Receptionist's Handbook
ISBN 0–7020–1834–1

Copyright © 1996 B.N.E. Quinn & P.P. Simons
Published by Baillière Tindall Ltd, London

(Child aged less than six years) Has child had all appropriate vaccinations?	Yes/No
Diabetic or asthmatic? (If YES, log to health promotion system and arrange appropriate appointment)	Diabetic : Yes/No Asthmatic : Yes/No
Are there any other family members who need to register?	Yes/No
Practice information leaflet given?	Yes/No
Practice charter given?	Yes/No
Medical history questionnaire?	Yes/No

The GP Receptionist's Handbook
ISBN 0–7020–1834–1

Copyright © 1996 B.N.E. Quinn & P.P. Simons
Published by Baillière Tindall Ltd, London

APPENDIX 5b:
Schedule of forms for patient records.
(Photocopy at 140% to achieve an A4 form)

Note: only the English form numbers are included in this table.

Item of record stationery	Number
Baby's first registration card	FP-58
Notification of patients added to list	Z68
Continuation card (female)	FP-8
Continuation card (male)	FP-7
Female record envelope ('Lloyd George' type)	FP-6
Gusseted record envelope	FP-5-B
Gusseted record envelope	FP-6-B
Immunisation record card	FP-1011
Male record envelope ('Lloyd George' type)	FP-5
Notification of patients removed from doctor's list	FP-22
Summary of patient treatment cards (male)	FP-9-A
Summary of patient treatment cards (female)	FP-9-B
Vaccination record card (male)	FP-7-A
Vaccination record card (female)	FP-8-A

The GP Receptionist's Handbook
ISBN 0-7020-1834-1

Copyright © 1996 B.N.E. Quinn & P.P. Simons
Published by Baillière Tindall Ltd, London

6

Communications Technology

Without communications general practice simply cannot run. The receptionist is there to be a link between the general public and the practice team. For this reason you need to have a command of the communications technology currently in use in most surgeries.

In this chapter you will learn:

1) Some useful points about telephones and telephone technique.

2) About more sophisticated devices such as pagers, mobile phones and answering machines.

3) A few basic points about use of fax machines.

INTRODUCTION

Modern technology now plays an increasing role in general practice, particularly in the area of communication. In this chapter we describe the items of technology which you will come across, starting with the one with which you will already be familiar – the telephone.

TELEPHONES AND TELEPHONE EXCHANGES

TELEPHONE 'DO'S' AND 'DON'TS'

- **Do** find out what the telephone 'greeting script' is for your surgery, 'e.g. '*Ashley Road, Surgery. Good morning, Sheila speaking*' or '*Doctors White, Green, Brown, and Black. . . .*' *Write it down and keep it with you so you can read from it if you can't remember it at first.*

- **Do** give an immediate apology for a late answer.

- **Do** get the caller's name – '*May I ask who's calling?*'

- **Do** check the caller's identity if they claim to be calling from the FHSA or the hospital. Ask for their name and department before giving them any information about patients.

- **Do** use the caller's name, if you can do so without giving away confidential information to anyone who could be within earshot. But **don't** repeat the caller's name loudly, especially if waiting patients can hear you.

- **Do** tell the caller what you're doing, e.g. '*I'll just make a note of this and look in our records*' or '*Would you mind holding on while I look for information in our records/ask the senior receptionist,*' etc.

- If you have to put the phone down, **do** tell the caller, e.g. '*I'll have to just put the phone done for a moment while I look for. . . .*'

- If you have to transfer a call to someone else's telephone, **do**:

    - Explain that the caller may have to wait.

    - Give call checks every 30 seconds or so – don't leave them hanging on. '*Still trying for you. . . .*'

    - If the caller has to wait, explain the waiting situation, e.g. '*Sorry to keep you Mrs Smith, but Dr Bloggs is still with a patient. I'll try again*'.

    - Offer a positive alternative, e.g. '*Can I phone you back as soon as the doctor is free or would you like to ring again at about 11 am?*'

- **Do** sum up or confirm what has been agreed at the end of the call, repeating names and telephone number (but making sure that no one can overhear sensitive information).

- **Do** make sure that information you give or receive is accurate. For example, it's very easy to confuse the letters 'f' and 's'. To ensure precision use the phonetic alphabet (Foxtrot for F and Sierra for S, etc.). The phonetic alphabet is listed in full in Appendix 6a at the end of this chapter. Avoid areas of confusion such as between '15' and '50' by saying 'one five' or 'five zero'. Similarly, you can avoid confusing '5' and '9' by pronouncing them very clearly, i.e. 'fife' and 'niner'.

■ **Do** take the trouble to find out how your practice telephones work. Each practice will have its own telephone set up but it's important to make sure that you master the following features of modern telephones:

  – Managing outside calls and routing them to the correct extension.
  – Putting the caller on 'hold' while you make enquiries.
  – Returning to an outside call after making an enquiry.
  – Setting the system up for an evening or night service, including call diversion if necessary.
  – Handling 'star key' and similar systems.

■ **Do** count to ten before answering the phone if for some reason you are angry or upset – otherwise callers will hear the anger in your voice.

■ **Do** smile before you use the phone. The callers will hear the smile in your voice. Try it!

■ **Don't** speak loudly when discussing patients' details if you can be overheard by patients in the waiting room.

■ **Don't** drop the phone, it sounds unprofessional. If you have to put the phone down for some reason tell the caller what you are doing.

■ **Don't** eat or drink whilst answering the phone – the caller can hear this!

■ **Don't** fumble for a pencil or say '*Hold on I'll just get a pencil and some paper*' – this hardly inspires confidence in the caller. Make sure you have paper and pencil to hand before you take the call.

■ **Don't** place your hand over the receiver if you want to have a private conversation with someone in the room and you don't want the caller to hear. It doesn't work! Modern telephone microphones are very sensitive and the caller can still hear what you are saying and it sounds awful! Instead use the 'mute', or 'hold' button that most modern phones have. This switches off the microphone at your end but you can still hear the caller.

■ **Don't** call people 'dearie' or 'luv'. Instead call them by their correct or desired names.

■ **Don't** use slang such as 'cheers' or 'bye'.

ANSWERING MACHINES

Using an answering machine in your practice

Many practices make use of answering machines to record messages out of hours or simply to give an announcement about which doctor is on call.

If you are expected to look after an answering machine make sure you are familiar with its use. Some answering machines will store all calls until you deliberately erase them. However, some machines will, once you have played back the messages, record over those messages later unless you deliberately instruct them not to.

The practice's doctors may have answering machines turned on during the working day (for example during the lunch break), and out of hours when they are out. There should always be a message for callers to hear. Some answering machines are quite sophisticated – when they take a message they automatically ring a number which sends a message to the doctor.

Make sure you know:

- How to avoid erasing messages accidentally.
- The procedures for writing down and acting on messages for the practice using a written register if necessary. This can be very important if a patient complains later that the practice did not respond to a message.
- How to check that the outgoing message is correct and clear.
- How to check that the incoming message tape has space on it.
- How to switch the answering machine off when it has already started to record an incoming message but you want to take the call.

Other people's answering machines

A lot of people have answering machines these days. So, before you dial, you need to *plan* your call to cover the possibility of having to leave a message. Your plan needs to include a long and short version of your message.

When the phone starts ringing at the other end of the line:

- listen for the answering machine itself to start up,
- when it does listen carefully to the directions,
- identify yourself immediately,

- give the date and time of the call,
- state the degree of urgency,
- state if you want the person to call back,
- give your number slowly and repeat it if you have time – remember someone at the other end will be trying to write it down!

PAGERS

Pagers are small devices that can be slipped into a handbag or clipped onto a pocket. They start bleeping when they are activated by a radio signal and are thus an ideal way of contacting a doctor wherever they are.

Pagers are of various degrees of sophistication:

- *Tone only* – you ring a telephone number which automatically triggers the pager's bleeper; the doctor then phones the surgery.

- *Answering machine type* – you ring a number and leave a message; the doctor's pager goes off; the doctor rings a different number and hears the message.

- *Display type, numbers only* – you ring a number; the pager gives a number only message.

- *Display type, brief message* – the pager bleeps and a message appears on a display screen on the pager.

- Pagers that are able to take messages generally have a limit on the length of the message, say no more than 60 characters.

Pagers are a lot cheaper than mobile phones and they are generally very reliable, but they have the disadvantage that the doctor has to find a telephone to answer the call.

MOBILE PHONES

Mobile phones are becoming more common as prices come down. They have a considerable advantage in that the doctor can be in immediate voice contact whilst driving or on a home visit.

They have some useful additional features. For example, if the phone is turned off or is not answered within a certain time, there is often a messaging facility whereby a caller can leave a message for the mobile phone subscriber to retrieve later.

The main problems with mobile phones are:

- Call charges are usually far higher than for ordinary telephones.
- They are not suitable for confidential discussions because conversations can be picked up by outsiders.
- The reception may be poor in some areas.

FAX MACHINES

A fax (short for 'facsimile') machine is a device which sends a document down a normal telephone line to a fax machine at the other end which prints it out. The process is just like an ordinary telephone call, except that instead of the human voice going down the telephone line with a receiver at each end it is an image of the document that is sent down the line. A fax machine converts the image to a form that can travel down the telephone wire.

The sorts of people or organisations you might be sending faxes to and receiving faxes from include:

- Insurance companies: enquiries and reports.
- Hospitals: referrals (especially urgent referrals) and reports.
- Branch surgeries.
- Suppliers.

The great advantage of a fax machine is that the recipient doesn't have to answer the phone – they can read the document at a convenient moment. In addition, not only can you send a lot more information more accurately than by phone, you can also send graphic images.

The key parts of a fax machine are:

- A number pad, just like that on a telephone.
- A small display screen, which often shows the number dialled and the progress of the call.
- Special keys for frequently dialled numbers which can be stored.
- A sheet feeder.
- An output tray.
- A telephone handset. (You can also use a fax machine for ordinary outgoing telephone calls.)

The advantage of fax machines is speedy written communication, which of course can include diagrams and pictures. As long as the document is in black and white, the fax machine can deal with it.

There are some disadvantages, the main one being that most machines print out the fax on special paper which is flimsy and can curl up. In addition, the actual image tends to fade fairly quickly. Also there are problems with sending documents that are printed on both sides. However, you can use a photocopier to solve both these problems – you can photocopy faxed messages when necessary for more a permanent copy, and if you want to send a double-sided sheet you can photocopy one side of the sheet.

How to use a fax machine

- Dial the number of the person to whom you are sending the fax. This sounds simple, but you need to take care that you dial the fax number and not the telephone number.

  You also need to make sure you are dialling the correct fax number, especially if you are sending confidential clinical information. You will probably see the number on the display, so that you can check the number before you actually send the fax.

- Most fax machines can electronically store the most frequently used fax numbers and you will be able to dial these by tapping just one or two keys.

- When you dial the number you will hear the normal dialling tone followed by a high pitched tone. The technical expression for this is *handshaking*, which means that the machine at the other end has recognised your machine and is ready to receive your fax message.

- If the machine has an automatic feeder this will then feed your document into the machine page by page. If not, you will have to feed the document in by hand.

  - Feed in your sheet of paper (usually A4 size). The important thing is to feed the paper in correctly so that the machine scans the side which has the text on it rather than the blank side! The best way to learn this is to do it yourself, perhaps by sending a 'test' message to another surgery under supervision.

  - Wait until one page has gone through before you send the next one. Make sure, however, that you have the next page ready to feed in straight away. If there is too long a pause between pages the fax machine will think that the message is complete and transmit only the first page.

■ Some machines will feed in your sheet of paper before they proceed to dial the number. They load the image of the sheet into their electronic memory. Then when they connect to the remote machine they can send the image more quickly, thus reducing the cost of the call.

■ If you get an 'engaged' tone when your machine has dialled, it means that the machine at the other end is busy sending out a fax or receiving one from another location. In this case you will have to try dialling again later. Some fax machines will automatically redial several times at set intervals until the other machine can accept the call.

■ When a fax is sent to you, don't pick up the phone on the fax machine as this may stop the incoming fax from arriving.

■ Some fax messages may contain confidential and sensitive information about patients. *Make sure that these incoming faxes do not lie around where anyone can see them.*

Other points about fax machines

Fax headers

A fax header is a form for you to fill in basic information about who you are sending the fax to, how many pages there are in the fax, etc. The header is normally sent as the first page so that the receiver has some basic information about the fax before it has been fully received.

Delayed transmission

With more sophisticated machines you can arrange to send a fax at a later time of day, for example, in the evening when telephone call charges are lower.

Splitters

Some subscribers use the same telephone line for both telephone and fax and have a special box called a 'splitter' which can detect if a fax or a phone call is being sent and will automatically route the call to either the telephone or the fax machine.

Make sure you understand how to send a fax. Ask if you can send the next practice fax under supervision.

PHOTOCOPIERS

Your practice may have a photocopier. It is important to remember not to leave the original document in the machine after you have finished copying. It may be a confidential document and an unauthorised person may discover and read it.

Make sure you know:

- how to deal with simple faults such as paper jams,
- how to replenish toner and paper, and
- who to contact if the machine breaks down. (Ideally a telephone number should be pinned to the wall near the machine).

It is also useful to know that in an emergency you can use the practice fax machine to make copies. Making copies in this way is time consuming and the quality is poor, but it may suffice in an emergency.

In this chapter you have learnt:

■ Basic telephone techniques.

■ Other telecommunications technology.

■ What fax machines do...

 — basic procedures for sending and receiving faxes, and
 — security precautions regarding incoming faxes.

APPENDIX 6a
The phonetic alphabet
As recommended by the International Civil Aviation Organisation

Alpha

Bravo

Charlie

Delta

Echo

Foxtrot

Golf

Hotel

India

Juliet

Kilo

Lima

Mike

November

Oscar

Papa

Quebec *(pronounced: Kay-beck)*

Romeo

Sierra

Tango

Uniform

Victor

Whiskey

Xray

Yankee

Zulu

7

Computers

Information technology plays an important role in general practice administration. In particular, the use of computers is now commonplace in most surgeries.

For the receptionist, handling computers is not a matter of 'being good with machines' but rather having the right approach. You won't be asked to be a technician, just a *user*, and if you are willing to try out new things and learn from your mistakes you are bound to succeed.

This chapter introduces you to information technology and how to approach it. It also provides you with a basic appreciation of computers, but you need to understand that systems vary from practice to practice.

In this chapter you will learn:

1) How to deal with any anxieties you may have about using computers.

2) What technology can do, e.g. what computers can be used for and what you are likely to be doing with them.

3) Some features of computers.

4) The importance of computer security and health and safety at the computer workstation.

5) Some common computer terminology.

INTRODUCTION

About 80% of practices now have computers. If your practice has six or more doctors or is a fundholding practice it's almost certain that some of its activities will be computerised. So it's unlikely that you can avoid coming into contact with computers.

You may feel some apprehension about getting to grips with 'technology', especially if you have not been employed for many years or haven't used a computer before. But experience has shown that, with practice, most people adapt readily to technology because modern computer systems are designed to be 'user-friendly'. By the end of this chapter you'll be more confident so that when you are first confronted with new technology it won't seem so strange or difficult.

Coping with 'technofear'

If you feel anxious about computers, try adopting this attitude. You can do anything that the computer can do – only the computer does it far, far more quickly.

Just as a shovel or a food-mixer can speed up our physical work, so think of the computer as a 'mind tool', doing things that humans can do, only more quickly. After all, you don't have to understand mechanics to use a car or be an electronics engineer to use a television, and it's the same with computers.

A last point to bear in mind is that most of your colleagues in the practice were once new to computing as well. They can be useful sources of advice, and are often better than the manuals.

This book cannot hope to explain everything about computers, but it does take you through some of the basics. The rest you can only learn with practice and training. You should try to set aside time to get experience of using the computer without the usual pressures of work.

WHAT COMPUTERS DO AND HOW THEY INVOLVE THE RECEPTIONIST

Computers are used mainly for their capacity to store information and sort information at tremendous speed. They can thus perform tasks that would take humans ages to do.

Computers can be used on their own ('stand-alone' computers) or connected by cables to other computers so that they can share information (a computer 'network').

In a typical practice with several thousand patients there is a vast amount of information, mainly related to patients' records. So in your practice you would probably find computers used for the following tasks.

Storing lots of information about patients – for example, basic details such as the sex, age and address of the several thousand patients in your practice – this is called an 'age–sex' register.

There is more information that a computer can store, for example:

Keeping a record of most drugs prescribed – this can be useful for surveys and reports. The additional advantage with computerised drugs records is that repeat prescriptions can be printed out quickly and accurately.

(Another advantage here is when it becomes known that clinical complications can arise with a certain drug, a computer system can call up a list of all patients taking that particular drug for action by the GP. This can be done far more rapidly than by hand.)

Keeping a record of basic procedures and treatments – for example, vaccinations and immunisations. This is very useful as the computer can then remind the doctor that a particular patient needs to have a vaccination.

Creating information – for example, sorting records and extracting information from them or reminding staff that things have to be done. This is especially important because GPs now have important contractual obligations. These include inviting all patients over 75 years of age for a yearly examination. Organising this would be very difficult without a computer.

General management of the practice – for example, sending letters, bookkeeping and financial activities, such as managing the payroll for all the practice staff and accounts.

Communications – another great advantage with computers is that they can be used not only to store information but also to transmit it quickly to other computers, thus allowing information to be shared. This can work in two ways.

Firstly, computers can be used to share information within the practice. We mentioned above that one or more computers can be linked up by cable. This is called a **network**. A network allows computers to share the same information. For example, a practice may have a network where one central computer holds patients' records such as drug and vaccination details. This information can be passed to other computers which are connected to it by special cables.

Practice staff working in different parts of the building on other computers which are connected to the central computer can view a patient's details on their screens and modify them to show, for example, that they have just had a tetanus vaccination. That information is then available straight away to other practice staff.

This network facility might be extended, for example, to a computer at a branch surgery so that up to date details are available to all the practice staff.

Secondly, computers can 'speak' to each other over long distances. Currently, many practices around the country are joining the FHSA Links project. This project allows the computers in individual practices to send data down telephone lines to the FHSA offices. This will mean that patient registration details and claims for payment can be sent electronically rather than having to be sent in bundles of paper by post. This will greatly speed up and simplify arrangements for keeping track of patients and payments.

WHAT DOES A COMPUTER CONSIST OF?

Figure 7.1 shows a diagram of a typical computer. More detail about computers is given in the glossary in Appendix 7a at the end of this chapter. The major components of a computer are described below.

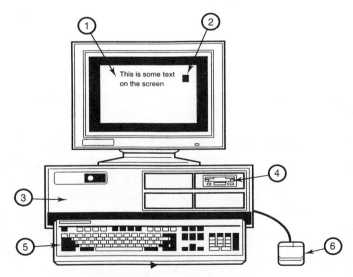

Figure 7.1 A typical computer
1, Screen; 2, Cursor; 3, System Unit; 4, Floppy disk drive; 5, Keyboard;
6, Mouse

The screen

The screen, often called the 'monitor', or the 'VDU' (visual display unit), is where the computer displays its information. Most screens in general practice can only display black and white, but some display colour.

You may see your screen go blank after a couple of minutes if no-one has touched the computer. Don't panic! This is because it has a 'screen saving' device that saves the screen from wearing out. You generally just need to press any keyboard key to get the screen to display again.

Most screens have controls for adjusting the brightness and contrast and also an ON/OFF switch. However, switching off the screen does not switch off the computer, so take care that if the computer needs to be completely shut down you know which controls to use.

The cursor

If you look closely at the screen you will see a small blinking square or line. This is called the cursor. Its function is to indicate where on the screen the typed characters will appear. When you type text into the computer it will appear at the same position as the cursor.

The system unit

This is the box that contains most of the workings of the computer including:

- A central processing unit where all the calculations and manipulations happen.
- A fixed storage device for permanently storing all the information the computer uses. This device is called a 'fixed' or 'hard' disk.

The system box usually includes an ON/OFF switch. You need to make sure you know how to switch the computer on and off properly. Switching off the computer screen alone is not enough to do this.

Floppy disk drive

This is where you can insert small disks (about 3½" in diameter) containing information. A modern floppy disk is in fact a thin plastic square, but inside its protective plastic case is a circle of flexible plastic. The surface of the disk is covered with a magnetic coating on which computer data can be stored. Unlike the fixed storage device mentioned above, floppy disks are portable and can be used to store information separately from the computer and to transfer information to other computers.

The keyboard

This is used to enter information into the computer. A computer keyboard has the same basic layout as a typewriter but with many additional keys. This is explained in more detail below.

The mouse

Some computers have a 'mouse'. This is a small device that can be used to move a pointer around the screen and for selecting information. Not all computers used in general practice can use a mouse.

The printer

Your computer will almost certainly be connected to a printer. The type of printer your practice uses will vary but you probably need to learn how to deal with minor problems.

Dot matrix printers use a collection of extremely small pins which are 'fired' through a ribbon. The pins are fired in a pattern which creates the letters. Your practice may also have laser printers which are very quiet and produce good quality print. If your practice has a 'network' of several computers it may be that they share one printer. This may mean that the printer output of your computer may take place in an office down the corridor.

If you have to use a computer printer find out about clearing paper blockages and loading fresh paper and/or toner. Try carrying out these tasks under supervision.

KEYBOARD LAYOUT

The computer keyboard layout is very similar to that of a typewriter, but there are some additional keys (see Figure 7.2).

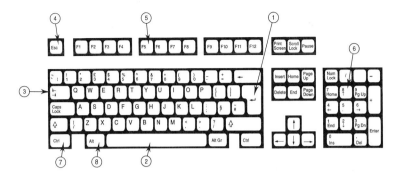

Figure 7.2 A typical computer keyboard
1, Enter key; 2, Space bar; 3, Tab key; 4, Escape key; 5, Function keys; 6, Number pad; 7, Ctrl key; 8, Alt key

If you have never used an electronic keyboard at all, you'll need to be aware that when you hold a key down it will carry on printing the same letter on the screen, so you need to keep a light touch!

If you have used a manual typewriter before you may be tempted to type the letter 'l' to indicate a numeral 'one' or a letter 'o' to indicate a numeral zero. Most computers don't like this and you may see a warning message. Make sure when typing numbers that you use either the keyboard number pad or the numbered keys.

Figure 7.2 shows a typical computer keyboard, but there can be slight variations. Some of the main keys which you need to be aware of are listed below.

The 'enter' or 'return' key

This is a very important key, but for some reason it is called by these two different names. Often the key itself is not named but has the symbol ⏎.

When you have finished typing something this key is normally used to send what you have typed to the computer. You may also find that if you are typing text using this key causes the cursor to drop down to the next line.

The space bar

This key will insert a space instead of character – just like a normal typewriter keyboard.

The tab key

This is very similar in function to a normal typewriter tab key. However, in some computer systems you press the tab key to jump around the different parts of the screen. We point this out here because some keyboards don't actually label this key as 'tab' but use a symbol of two opposing arrows $\overset{\leftarrow}{\rightarrow}$.

The escape key

This key is often marked 'Esc'. With most computer systems you may find that the escape key does something very similar to its name.

The computer performs its tasks by taking you through a series of steps. Sometimes you have to choose which step to take by selecting it from a menu displayed on the screen. The escape key allows you to move backwards rather than forwards through this path, so that you have the sensation of 'escaping' from the forward march of the program.

The function keys

These are numbered F1 to F12 and are placed above the top row of keys. The programs that your computer uses sometimes makes use of some of the function keys to perform special tasks.

The use of the keys will vary but, for example, many programs allow you to request a help message by pressing the F1 key.

Number pad

This allows you to enter numbers directly into the computer by touch typing, rather than using the row of numbers at the top of the keyboard. This is especially useful when entering large amounts of financial information. Do *not* be tempted to use alphabetical letters such as 'l' instead of '1' or 'o' instead of '0'.

The 'Ctrl' and 'Alt' keys

These keys ('Ctrl' is pronounced 'control') make the basic keyboard more versatile by extending the range of information it can send. They operate in the same way as the shift key on a normal keyboard allows you to access upper case (capital) letters or symbols such as £ and % above the numerals. For example, when you hold down the 'Alt' key and then press a normal key such as 'b', a special signal is sent to the computer which is not the same as a lower case or upper case 'b'. Computer programs use this facility to increase the range of commands that you can type in.

You need to pay attention when computer programs ask you to press a combination of two keys. A typical instruction might be 'Press Ctrl-b'. Sometimes this means you need to press both keys simultaneously. On a computer keyboard this means that you have to *hold down* one key, and then lightly tap the other one, keeping the first key held down. Sometimes you need to press and release one key, followed by another.

You need to make sure you understand both keyboard techniques – ask someone to demonstrate this for you on the keyboard if you are not quite sure.

Familiarise yourself with the basic keyboard layout of your practice's computers.

USING THE COMPUTER

'Computer courtesy'

If a patient is present whilst you are using the computer it is easy to give the impression that you are more interested in the computer than the patient! Or, even worse, the patient may get the impression that some kind of secret details about them are being held on the computer. Looking at the patient occasionally and explaining what you are doing should help to allay their fears. For example, '*I'm just making sure we've got your basic details right*' or '*I'm checking to see that your records are up to date*' or '*I'll just put your latest details on your record*', will help to reassure patients.

Using the screen or 'monitor'

Take great care when reading off the screen – it's a lot easier to misread text on a screen than that on paper, and it's a lot easier to miss your typing mistakes on a screen.

Take care about data entry. People usually believe what they see on the computer screen. Double check what you enter because later on even rubbish may be taken seriously by a future user.

Keeping the computer clean

Avoid drinking coffee or tea, etc., near the computer. Any fluid spilt onto the keyboard or computer can easily ruin it.

Take the time to keep the keyboard and screen clean. This makes the computer much more pleasant to use.

COMPUTERS AND SECURITY

Why security?

A general practice computer system contains information about patients that is strictly confidential and nobody other than practice staff should be allowed access to it. If information from records falls into the wrong hands or is accidentally destroyed the results could be disastrous for the practice and the patients.

What sort of security precautions are used?

This covers two areas:

− preventing unauthorised people from using the computer (security of access), and

− preventing information from being lost or damaged in some way (security of information).

These are dealt with in detail below.

Security of access

If you are required to use a computer, a member of staff will register you with the computer system so that the system can recognise you as a user. You will very probably be asked to think up a password to enter into the computer. This password will allow you (and only you) to use the computer under your own name.

With some systems you may find that you have been assigned a temporary password that will expire after a brief number of uses or within a few days. You then have to create your own new password.

When thinking up a password to use, bear in mind the following points:

- Don't use your first name or nickname, or the names of your children. There is a slight risk that another member of staff may attempt to guess your password and use it. Also there is a chance that the computer may be stolen by a thief who may try to read patient information from the computer. The thief may know the surgery and know your name.

- Similarly, don't use a password based on the registration number of your car.

- Don't use a password which is so obscure that you forget it almost immediately!

Every time you use the computer you will have to enter your name and password. This is called **logging on** or 'logging in'. You may see the prompt 'login' on the screen. Once you have logged on, the computer will allow you to access the data that the practice considers appropriate for your work.

It's important that you, and only you, use the computer under your own name. Within the practice different grades of staff may have different 'levels' of access. For example, the computer system may give the doctors access to clinical information about the patient that is not accessible to other grades of staff. Additionally some grades of staff may be allowed to *look* at information but *not amend it*.

It may happen that while you are using the computer you have to leave the computer for a few minutes. In this situation it is very important that you **log off** or 'log out' before walking away. It's important to do this because someone else could easily use the computer while you are away. The password is your computerised signature, and in such a situation the computer cannot tell if the user is *not* you, and will allow that person to get information that they may not be entitled to.

Because the computer keeps a record of who logged on and when, you could get the blame for this.

Do *not* be tempted to let another member of staff use your password or start using the computer before you have logged off properly.

Some systems record the initials of the user who adds new data or amends existing data. If you allow others to use a terminal that you are logged into, you might get the blame for something you did not do.

On some systems, the use of your password allows you to access your electronic mail. Electronic mail, or email, is a way of sending messages to people or groups of people using the computer. Most of the electronic mail circulating on the practice's computer system is simply information about practice activities, but you may also receive messages of a personal nature that you would not want others to see.

When you leave a terminal you should ensure that no one could use the terminal with your password. You should log out.

Make sure you are clear about your password, how to enter it, and how to change it. Try logging on and off with your new password under supervision.

Some computers can tell automatically if no one has used them for a while and will automatically switch themselves off after 2 or 3 minutes. (This is not the same as the 'screen saver' feature mentioned earlier.) However, it's better not to wait for the computer to do this but to log off as soon as you leave.

Take care with printers and printout. Don't throw printout into a wastepaper bin if it has patients' details on it. Your practice may have a shredding machine for this.

Security of data (often called data integrity)

The data on the computer is not just at risk from falling into the wrong hands. It can be physically damaged or corrupted in some way. In particular it is at risk from computer viruses, theft and sudden data loss.

Computer viruses

You may have heard about computer viruses. These have nothing in common with the clinical viruses that some of your patients may suffer from! Instead, viruses are special computer programs that are surreptitiously placed into systems, sometimes as a practical joke but often with malicious intent. Viruses can replicate and spread themselves by moving around computer systems (hence the term 'virus').

You must take viruses seriously because the consequence of having a virus on your practice's computer system could mean that all the data are erased or corrupted, or the entire system is made unusable.

Viruses are often spread via 'free' software given away by computer magazines and from other sources.

All practices using computers should possess special computer programs which can detect viruses and eliminate them. However, new viruses are constantly appearing and some of them can avoid detection. To make sure that you do not accidentally transfer a computer virus to the practice system you need to take the following precautions:

■ Don't use any disks containing computer games from your home or from computer magazines in a practice computer.

■ Your practice may receive disks through the post containing sample computer programs. Do not use these on a practice computer without first checking with the practice manager or someone responsible for looking after the computers.

■ You may be given disks which contain data to copy onto the system. Where you have to use floppy disks make sure you follow procedures set by the practice for checking disks for viruses.

Ask if there is a practice policy about computer virus protection. If you are required to use a virus protection program, ask to be shown how to work it.

Theft

Computers are tempting to thieves who may be more interested in selling them than trying to look at the data. The impact of the loss of computers would be catastrophic for the clinical care of the patients.

Most practices will have some kind of system for preventing unauthorised access to technical equipment. You must be prepared to co-operate with security measures such as locking rooms where computers are kept.

Corruption or sudden data loss

Computers hold information in their electronic 'memories' which need a continuous supply of electricity to retain it. Something you need to be aware of is to be *careful about unplugging any item of electrical equipment.* It could be a vital piece of computer equipment, and removing the electricity supply suddenly could cause important information to be lost. A sudden shutdown like this could also cause the data and programs already stored on the computer's hard disk to be corrupted in some way.

Making 'back-ups'

One way in which the practice can protect against theft or corruption of data is by means of 'back-ups'. These are simply duplicate copies of the computer's data. The duplicate copies are made regularly (often daily) so that if anything goes seriously wrong the previous day's back-up copy can be re-installed on the computer, and a maximum of only one day's work would be lost.

The duplicated copy can be made in various ways, but the most common is by means of magnetic tape. These tapes look like the music cassettes you find in a hi-fi system, only a bit larger. They can store lots of computer data, and if the computers go wrong or break down then the tapes can be used to play back the data to the replacement computers.

HEALTH AND SAFETY

If you use the computer for long periods at a time you should be aware of EC Directive 90/270 on Display Screen Equipment which came into effect on 1 January 1993. The Directive lays down strict minimum requirements and your employer does not have discretion on whether or not to implement it.

The Directive covers employees (including people on short-term contracts), who *have* to use computers regularly for *concentrated periods*.

Because your use of computers may only be for a few minutes at a time you may find that you are not covered by these regulations. However, you ought to be aware of the provisions of these regulations.

- **Screen (VDU)** The screen should be adjustable so that you can tilt it up or down or from side to side. The screen should also be glare-free and of a type known as 'low radiation'.
- **Desks** Desks should be of an adequate size and of a comfortable height.
- **Chair** This should give adequate lumbar support and be adjustable in all directions.
- **Document holders** These should be provided so that you can support a document you are copying from close to the screen. This saves you from constantly looking down at text on the desk and then back to the screen.
- **Further regulations** These govern room layout and heating and ventilation, noise, and electrical safety.

Employers have until the end of 1996 to upgrade existing equipment so that it meets the above requirements.

In addition regular eye and eyesight tests must be made available, and the costs for these, including correct appliances, must be met by your employer.

If you are permanently working on a computer your routine at the computer should not exceed 90 minutes without a break – it makes sense to take a break before fatigue sets in.

You should also take precautions yourself. The following tips have been extracted from *Working with VDUs* published by the Health and Safety Executive:

- Adjust your chair and VDU to find the most comfortable position for your work. As a broad guide, your arms should be approximately horizontal and your eyes at the same height as the top of the VDU casing.

- Make sure there is enough space underneath your desk to move your legs freely. Move any obstacles such as boxes or equipment.

- Avoid excess pressure on the backs of your legs and knees. A footrest may be helpful.

- Don't sit in the same position for long periods. Make sure you change your posture as often as is practicable. Some movement is desirable, but avoid stretching movements.

- Adjust your keyboard and screen to get a good keying and viewing position. A space in front of the keyboard is sometimes helpful for resting the hands and wrists when not keying.

- Don't bend your hands up at the wrist when keying. Try to keep a soft touch on the keys and don't overstretch your fingers. Good keyboard technique is important.

- Try different layouts of the keyboard, screen and document holder to find the best arrangement for you.

- Make sure you have enough work space to take whatever documents you need. A document holder may help you to avoid awkward neck movements.

- Arrange your desk and screen so that bright lights are not reflected in the screen. You shouldn't be directly facing windows or bright lights. Adjust curtains or blinds to prevent unwanted light.

- Make sure the characters on your screen are sharply focused and can be read easily. They shouldn't flicker or move.

- Make sure there are no layers of dirt, grime or finger marks on the screen.

- Use the brightness control on the screen to suit the lighting conditions in the room.

1) Find out where the computer manual is kept and if it has a beginner's section.

2) Find out who is the person to contact when you have problems with the computer, and who is responsible for computer training.

3) Find out the name of the person or supplier who provides telephone help for problems with your practice's computers.

You should now have some idea of:

■ The basic components of a computer – screen, monitor, keyboard, hard disk, networks and their advantages.

■ What these basic computer activities mean:

– entering data,

– saving data,

– back-ups,

– printing out,

– logging on and off, and

– entering passwords.

■ The proper use of computers:

– password security and different levels of password security,

– health and safety issues affecting computers, and

– data protection.

APPENDIX 7a
Glossary of simple computer terminology

We can't hope to cover the entire world of computer knowledge in this glossary, but we give explanations of some terms you may come across in your first few months. You won't become a computer expert by reading this glossary. But you will be slightly less puzzled by all the jargon you hear if you can refer to this glossary from time to time.

ASCII (pronounced ass-key) – American Standard Code for Information Interchange. ASCII files are a standard for computer files. Because the format is so widely used and 'understood' by all sorts of programs, ASCII files are frequently used to exchange information between programs and computers. Because ASCII files consist of plain text only, features such as bold or italic text cannot be handled.

Back-up – making a duplicate copy of the data in a computer's storage system in case the original gets damaged. Most computers use magnetic disks to store vast amounts of data. Unfortunately these data are constantly at risk of being lost. There is always a risk that the magnetic disk may fail to work because it is damaged in some way. This may corrupt or destroy the data. There is also the risk that the computer itself may break down and it may not be able to 'read' the data from its hard disk. For this reason the person in charge of your practice's computers should always make back-ups daily. This means that, should the data in the computer be lost, there is a spare copy of the data that was made on the previous day to fall back on.

Boot, booting, and re-booting – to load a program or an operating system into the computer's memory.

Bytes, kilobytes, megabytes, etc. – measurements of computer file size. For example, a single character of the alphabet requires one byte of storage space. A kilobyte is approximately 1000 bytes. A page of simple correspondence would need about three to five kilobytes of storage space. A megabyte is about one million bytes and would store about six hundred A4 pages of text.

CD-ROM – a CD-ROM looks very much like a compact disc that is used in domestic hi-fi systems. In fact they differ slightly because they contain very large amounts of data. For example, a single CD-ROM can hold the equivalent of 750 000 pages of text. CD-ROMs can be used in a modern computer providing it has a special CD-ROM drive which can cost less than £200 to install. You may find CD-ROMs in your practice being used by the doctors as a fast information retrieval system for details of drugs or for clinical information.

CPU – central processing unit. This is the bit of hardware that does the work of carrying out the computing commands. In other words it is the place where the computer does its thinking.

Cursor – the small flashing highlighted square on your computer monitor. If you are typing it moves as you type and shows you where the next character you type will appear. If you are using a mouse the cursor may appear on the screen as an arrow.

Database – if you use a computer in your practice you are probably working on a data base. A data base is an organised collection of information rather like a card index, except that the computer's data base is far more sophisticated and powerful to use.

Default – this term is used in the sense of 'going by default'. The term 'default value' means a pre-determined value which the computer system will use if a different value is not specified.

Directory – a section of a computer's storage space. Think of a directory rather like the drawer of a filing cabinet. Files are put into different directories so that they are easier to organise.

Disks – computers use disks to store data. Most disks store the data magnetically. There are two main types of disk you need to know about:

■ Floppy disks – most 'floppy' disks are about 3.5" in diameter and are protected by an almost rigid plastic case which is far from floppy. However, the name survives because of its predecessors which were indeed 'floppy'. Floppy disks are removable storage devices which can store both programs and data. Most disks can store the equivalent of about 400 A4 pages of text.

■ Hard (or 'fixed') disks – unlike disks, hard disks are fixed inside the computer and are not removable. Because the hard disks are rigid and can spin very rapidly they can hold much more data and transmit it far more rapidly than a floppy disk, can.

Enter – another name given to the keyboard 'return' key. In fact you will often find these two names used interchangeably.

Field – a category of data in a data base. For example the computer record for Mr Fred Bloggs will have a name field, an address field, and so on.

Files – computers organise all their data into files. For example, a letter or document will exist in the form of a file with its own name such as BLOGGS.LET.

Fileserver – if your practice has a computer network, there may be one computer set aside to hold the majority of the practice's information and to 'serve' that information to the other computers which are connected to it. This computer is usually called a fileserver and will have a great deal of storage space on its hard disk. You may find that the fileserver is kept in a secure room away from the public areas of the surgery.

Function keys – the set of 12 keys, usually on the top row of the keyboard and labelled F1 to F12. The purpose of these keys varies from program to program.

Hardware – as the name implies, the hardware is all the parts of the computer that you can see and touch. It includes things like the disk drives, the central processor and the electronic memory.

Interface – a software or hardware connection for the transmission of data between hardware or software.

RAM – random access memory (or just 'memory'). The RAM forms a temporary electronic store for digital codes. When the computer is switched off the RAM is emptied.

Menu – a menu offers you a choice of different options on screen. Generally you use the arrow keys (or 'cursor' keys) on your keyboard to highlight your menu choice and then use the Enter key to select it.

Modem – a device which converts computer signals to signals that can be sent down an ordinary telephone line. This allows the computer to 'talk' to computers in other parts of the country without having to use special cable.

Monitor – another word for the computer screen.

Mouse – a device for pointing at items on the computer screen. It is a hand-held device that you can roll about on your desk top and which moves a pointer (or 'cursor') on the screen. Mice usually have one or two buttons that you click to select something on the screen. Mice are more frequently used with graphical screen designs.

Network – a number of computers connected together by special cable and sharing information.

Operating system – the computer program that does all the basic work of running the computer and controlling the flow of information between all the different bits of the computer. It takes care of file handling, the use of the computer's memory and sending data to the screen and the printer. The software that you use runs on top of this basic layer. Typical names of operating systems that you may come across are Dos, Unix, Xenix, Novell and Windows.

PC – personal computer. Most computers that you will meet in general practice are PCs. PCs can be used on an ordinary desk top rather than in a special installation.

Peripherals – an overall term for all the devices that the computer uses to send and receive data. For example, the computer's monitor, printer, and keyboard are all peripherals.

Ports – the special sockets at the back of the computer that cables from peripherals can be plugged in to. There are two main types of port:

■ Parallel port – this is generally used to connect the computer to a printer.

■ Serial port – this is generally used to connect the computer to a modem or a mouse.

Prompt – a visual sign from the computer asking you to enter some information.

Record – all the data pertaining to one item. For example, all the data on Mr Fred Bloggs (his name, address, phone number, date of birth, etc.) makes up a record.

Return – this term is a relic from the era when the key labelled carriage return on a typewriter was used to return to the beginning of the line. On a modern computer it is the name sometimes given to the key that sends the data you have typed to the computer for action.

Software – the sets of logical instructions that control the functioning of the computer.

Spreadsheet – a program which is mainly used to manipulate numbers. It allows the user to enter figures into rows and columns on screen and then perform mathematical calculations. It is thus very useful for financial and statistical calculations.

UPS – uninterruptible power supply. If the mains electricity supply to a computer is suddenly cut off, a computer can lose vital data in its electronic memory. The UPS is a device which protects a computer from a sudden loss or surge of Mains electricity. You may find that your practice's file server is equipped with a UPS.

VDU – visual display unit, i.e. the computer screen.

Word-processor – a program that handles text. Unlike a typewriter or hand-writing, a word-processing program allows you to move text around, delete it, and rearrange it on the screen without having to retype the whole page. Some programs check for correct spelling and grammar.

FHSA Forms

This chapter deals with many of the commonly used forms for claiming fees from the Family Health Services Authority (FHSA). Filling in forms is a significant part of your reception activities. In fact sometimes you'll think that forms are the sole reason for the existence of the general practice receptionist! Eventually, many of the paper forms will be replaced by the use of computers to transmit claims to FHSAs electronically. However, you still need an understanding of the circumstances under which the practice can claim fees and what the various claims are.

By the end of this chapter you will know about the forms that you will need to use most of the time. In addition, you will have an understanding of why and when these forms are needed.

In this chapter you will learn:

1) Why forms are used.

2) What situations call for a form to be filled in and which form should be used.

3) Things to look out for when filling in forms.

4) The importance of accuracy.

Before you start – find out where the forms listed in this chapter are kept and who you should contact when stocks of forms need replenishing.

INTRODUCTION

Forms are used to transmit claims for payments between the surgery and the authorities who pay the doctor. Forms are used either:

- to request payments for items of medical service, or
- to notify the FHSA of changes to the doctor's list.

Because forms usually have to be signed by the patient and sometimes by the doctor, they represent an official way of verifying that a particular service has been given.

✓ It's very important that you record details *accurately* on forms; for example, the patient's date of birth. This information can determine what kind of service the GP can offer the patient and what payments the GP can receive. The GP must claim correctly for the items of service offered as any mistakes can affect both the patient's care and the GP's income.

In this chapter you'll find the most commonly occurring situations that require a form to be filled in, together with details of each form. We haven't covered every form you'll come across in general practice. Some of the forms you read about here will be mentioned again in separate chapters such as those on vaccination (Chapter 13), medical certificates (Chapter 9), contraception (Chapter 14) and maternity (Chapter 15).

See also Chapter 6 where electronic messaging is covered in more detail

You may find that your surgery uses electronic messaging by computer to transmit and receive registration details between your practice and the FHSA. This system is called **GP Links** and is already in many practices throughout the UK. GP Links is being extended to include claims for item of service payments. If your surgery uses GP Links you still need to understand the information in this chapter about the different types of claims GPs can make.

Appendices 8a and 8b at the end of this chapter give a handy schedule of all the forms mentioned here.

We deal first with forms used for registration and then with the most common item of service claim forms.

REGISTRATION

There are four types of registration:

1) Normal registration.
2) Temporary registration.
3) Emergency treatment.
4) Immediately necessary treatment.

Items (3) and (4) are not strictly registrations, but they are ways in which a GP can treat a patient under the NHS.

Normal registration

Most new patients simply turn up at the surgery and ask to join a doctor's list. Often a parent will arrive and want to register their entire family. Some people remember to bring their medical card with them.

Normally patients who wish to register with a GP must *intend* to be resident in the locality for more than 3 months and should provide their medical card or NHS number.

For registering new patients the preferred document is the form **FP-4** which is the patient's own medical card. However, if the patient forgets to bring their own medical card with them when they come to register then you should ask them to sign a form **FP-1** (in Scotland **GP-1**; in Northern Ireland, **HS-22**). It is important to send this form off to the FHSA as soon as possible. A GP is responsible for the medical care of a patient once that patient has been accepted, even if the FHSA has not yet been informed.

If the patient is a new-born baby then the parents will bring a form **FP-58** (In Scotland, **GP-58**; in Northern Ireland, **HS-123**), which is given to them by the Registrar of Births and Deaths when they register the birth. Children under 16 years of age should be registered by their parents.

If the patient has been discharged from the armed forces, form **FP-13** should be used. If this form is not available, use form **FP-1**.

GPs do not have to accept a patient if they don't want to. Some GPs like to interview all patients before accepting them on their list.

Find out what procedures or guidelines the GPs in your surgery have for new patients. For example, do they accept all patients without exception, or do they prefer to interview them first?

The GP may also refuse to accept a patient if the patient lives outside the geographical area covered by the GP's surgery. This area is usually clearly defined.

> Find out the geographical area covered by your surgery and if the GPs will accept patients from outside that area.

Some GPs in your surgery may have 'closed' their list. This means that they do not want to accept any more patients on their normal list and will only accept new registrations under exceptional circumstances. For example they may agree to accept the relatives of existing patients as new patients.

> Find out which GPs have 'closed' lists and which are still accepting patients.

A GP can refuse to accept a patient on the normal list. However, if required, the GP has to give the patient whatever treatment is necessary. This aspect is dealt with later in this chapter.

You may find that your practice has a set of procedures (often called a 'protocol') for the management of new patient applications.

Patients who cannot find a GP to accept them on their list can ask the FHSA to *allocate* them to a GP's list.

In metropolitan areas such as London there may be a large number of patients from abroad who wish to register. They may have to prove that they are eligible for NHS treatment (e.g. by proving that they are normally resident in the UK). A GP can exercise a large amount of discretion in accepting foreign nationals on his or her list.

New patient examination fee

When a GP accepts a patient onto the normal list he or she is obliged to offer that patient a New Patient Examination. However the patient is not obliged to take up this offer. If arranged, the examination should be carried out within 3 months of the patient being accepted. Form **FP/RF** (in Scotland, **GP/RF**; in Northern Ireland, **RF**) is used for claiming this fee. If the examination is delayed for up to 12 months from the patient being accepted then the GP can still claim the fee if he or she can give good reason for the delay.

The GP has to write to the patient within 28 days of registration inviting the patient to attend for a New Patient Examination. One of the options here is to have a supply of blank invitation letters at the reception desk for this purpose. Sometimes patients are reluctant to attend for these examinations so you may find it more persuasive to use phrases such as 'This is a chance for you to meet your new doctor' or 'This is an opportunity for us to get to know a bit more about you'. Alternatively, you could just ask 'When would you like your New Patient Examination?'

Most GPs delegate the New Patient Examinations work to the practice nurse.

Find out how the New Patient Examinations are arranged in your practice.

The GP cannot claim a New Patient Examination fee if the patient is under 5 years old. In this case your GP may, if on the Child Health Surveillance list, offer **Child Health Surveillance** to the parents (see the section on Child Health Surveillance later in this chapter).

Also, the GP cannot claim a New Patient Examination fee if the patient was previously on the list of a partner of the GP and was given a New Patient Examination by that partner within the previous 12 months.

In some circumstances the GP may find that there are a very large number of patients who require an examination. This usually happens if another GP dies or retires and patients are reallocated to other GPs. In these circumstances the GP can ask the FHSA to allow for extension of the time period.

Temporary registration

If someone is staying in an area for just a short time, they can get medical treatment from a GP as a **temporary resident**. Typical examples are: a student home during university holidays, a daughter visiting her parents for a few days, or a family on holiday in the locality.

The temporary registration facility allows the general public to be mobile throughout the UK without having to worry about medical care.

Temporary residents are those who intend to stay in the locality for *longer than 24 hours from the date of treatment*. (Those who are in the locality for less than 24 hours are dealt with under Emergency

Treatment – see the section on emergency treatment later in this chapter.) (In Scotland special arrangements apply for Oil Rig workers and merchant seamen who are in the district for less than 24 hours.)

The form used to claim for a temporary resident is **FP-19** (in Scotland, **GP-19**; in Northern Ireland, **HS-15**).

You need to tick a box on the FP-19 to show how long the patient *intends* to stay in the locality. This is either

■ 2–15 days from the first treatment, *or* 16 days to 3 months from the first treatment.

The GP receives a higher fee if the patient is staying for longer than 15 days so it's important to be accurate about this.

The FP-19 is a two-part form. You should send the top copy to the FHSA straight away. The bottom copy is kept at the surgery until the end of the patient's stay. The back part of the form includes a space for the doctor to make clinical notes.

Most surgeries will keep all the temporary registration forms in one place until the patient has left the locality.

Find out where the temporary registration forms are kept in your surgery and what procedures there are for sending them to the FHSA once the patient is no longer being treated.

Sometimes a patient who originally intended to stay for up to 15 days stays on for a further period. In this case the GP should send in a further FP-19 marked 'amended'.

It is useful to write the date of expiry of the FP-19 at the bottom of the clinical notes section. This makes it easy to see when this section should be sent on to the FHSA. If the patient should extend their stay in your area and present for further clinical care, having the expiry date on the form enables you quickly to see that the form has expired and that you need to get another one signed.

If a patient intends to stay for longer than 3 months in the locality then he or she should go on the GP's normal list of patients.

If the patient says that they intend to stay in the locality for less than 3 months but then actually stays for longer than 3 months but less than 6 months, the FHSA will accept a second FP-19 which should be marked 'extended stay'.

A woman can ask to receive contraceptive treatment or maternity care as a temporary resident.

A GP can refuse to accept a patient as a Temporary Resident (see below).

In some cases the GP may not be eligible for a temporary resident fee. This is the case where the *only* treatment provided was a vaccination, immunisation, contraceptive service or maternity service and no general medical service was provided.

Emergency treatment

Emergency fees are only paid for treatment given to patients intending to stay *less than 24 hours* in the locality. (In Scotland, special arrangements apply for Oil Rig workers and merchant seamen who are in the district for less than 24 hours.)

There are two other situations where a GP can claim an emergency treatment fee:

- Where the GP has to give urgent treatment to a patient who is registered with another local GP but for some reason cannot contact that GP, perhaps because there is some problem with the telephone or the GP has fallen ill suddenly.
- If a GP is called to attend someone who urgently requires medical attention (e.g. someone who has collapsed in the street).

Form **FP-32** (in Scotland, **GP-32**; in Northern Ireland, **HS-14**) can be used to claim an emergency treatment fee.

Fees cover the treatment of fractures, dislocations or giving an emergency consultation. However, the treatment must be given *within* the GP's practice area.

If the patient was involved in an accident with a motor vehicle then the GP has to recover his or her fee from the driver of the vehicle. If unsuccessful, the GP can then try to claim from the FHSA.

Note that the GP cannot claim emergency fees for patients on his or her normal list because this is already covered by the capitation fee.

Immediately necessary treatment

A GP cannot turn away a patient needing treatment.

Form **FP-106** (in Scotland, **GP-105**; in Northern Ireland, **HS-14T**) is used when GPs give treatment that is immediately necessary to a patient whom they have refused either to accept onto their normal list, or to accept as a temporary resident.

There may be situations where a GP accepts a patient onto the normal list within 3 months of giving that patient immediately necessary treatment. For example, the FHSA may assign the patient to the GP. In this case the immediately necessary treatment fee is still payable.

If, however, the GP voluntarily accepts the patient onto the normal list then the patient is considered by the FHSA to have been on the normal list from the first day of treatment and the immediately necessary treatment fee is not claimable.

OTHER ITEMS OF SERVICE

Maternity services

A pregnant woman can register with a GP (even if it is not her own GP) for maternity services. The GP can claim fees for ante- and post-natal care, and for care during the confinement. Women who are temporarily resident in an area can also receive maternity services from a GP in that area. This gives mobility to mothers-to-be.

The form to use for recording all maternity claims is **FP-24** (in Scotland, **GP-24**; in Northern Ireland, **MMS1**). If the GP is not on the Obstetric List held by the FHSA then **Form FP-24-A** is used. This is identical to form FP-24 but is coloured pink. (In Scotland, form **GP-24-A**; in Northern Ireland, only GPs on the Obstetric List can claim for provision of maternity services.)

Ante-natal care

For ante-natal care the GP's fees vary according to how early on in the pregnancy the woman is accepted for maternity services. It is therefore important to get the patient to sign the form as soon as possible, or the GP's fees may be reduced. If the woman is a temporary resident the FHSA will pay a proportionate amount depending on the length of time for which the GP is responsible for maternity care. Therefore the dates of the first and last service need to be carefully recorded on the FP-24.

Confinement fee

If a GP attends a woman in labour he or she can claim a confinement fee, whether or not she is registered with that GP for maternity services.

A confinement fee is also payable if there is a stillbirth after the 28th week of pregnancy and the woman had arranged maternity services with that GP.

Miscarriage fee

The GP can claim a miscarriage fee if a woman who has arranged maternity services with them has a miscarriage before the 28th week of pregnancy.

If the woman did *not* make arrangements for maternity services, the GP can claim a miscarriage fee if a miscarriage occurs after the 8th week of pregnancy.

Post-natal care

Post-natal care fees consist of two elements:

Post-natal visits – the GP can claim for up to five post-natal visits to the mother and the child. This applies even if the mother gave birth in hospital.

Post-natal examination fees – the GP can claim a fee for a post-natal examination as long as it is carried out between 6 and 12 weeks after the confinement. If the examination is delayed beyond this period the GP can still claim the fee if a good reason for the delay can be given.

Therapeutic abortion

If a woman has arranged maternity care with a GP and subsequently undergoes a therapeutic abortion, the GP can claim a miscarriage fee. If no arrangements were made with a GP then no maternity fees can be claimed.

There are no maternity fees payable for the aftercare of women who have had an abortion.

Find out which GPs in your practice are on the FHSA Obstetric List.

Contraceptive care

A woman can receive contraceptive services from:

- her own GP, or
- any GP in the locality who is prepared to provide contraceptive services.

Normal contraceptive service

The main form for contraceptive services is **FP-1001** (in Scotland, **GP-102**; in Northern Ireland, **FP-1001**). This form is used for all ordinary services such as:

- accepting the patient on the contraceptive list,
- giving advice,
- conducting any necessary examination,
- where appropriate, prescribing drugs or an occlusive cap, and
- providing any follow-up care.

The FP-1001 covers ordinary contraceptive services and advice. Payment is made to the GP for 12 months from the date when the patient *applied* for the service rather than the date when any treatment was given. Therefore it is important to get the FP-1001 signed as soon as possible.

After 12 months of service a further FP-1001 needs to be signed if contraceptive services are still being provided. However, the further form can actually be signed between 11 and 18 months after the first. This allows for the patient not attending for a check-up exactly 12 months after the form was signed.

Find out what arrangements are made in your surgery to make sure that form FP-1001 is renewed after 1 year.

Intrauterine device

If the GP fits an intrauterine device (IUCD) a higher payment is made and a different form is used. This is form **FP-1002** (in Scotland, **GP-103**; in Northern Ireland, **FP-1002**). Form FP-1002 only applies if the GP (or a partner or associate of the GP) fits the IUCD.

If the GP does not actually fit the IUCD and instead refers the patient to an NHS or Family Planning Association clinic, form **FP-1001** is used.

Form FP-1002 only covers 12 months from the first fitting of an IUCD. After this time an FP-1001 form should be used unless the IUCD is replaced.

Contraceptive services for temporary residents

A woman can receive a contraceptive service from any GP within the locality where she is temporarily staying. Form **FP-1003** (in Scotland, **GP-104**; in Northern Ireland, **FP-1003**) is used for this.

If an IUCD is fitted by the GP then an FP-1003 form is still used, but with an appropriate declaration by the GP.

The important thing to remember about contraceptive services to temporary residents is that the Temporary Resident form (FP-19) should not be submitted in addition to the FP-1003 if the *only* service given to the patient was a contraceptive one.

Night visits

Every time a GP is called out to one of the patients on his or her list *between the hours of 10 pm and 8 am* a **night visit fee** can be claimed using form **FP-81** (in Scotland, **GP-81**; in Northern Ireland, **NV-1**).

A GP can claim a fee for every patient he or she sees at one location (although the fees do not increase exactly in proportion to the number of patients). However, visits to a mother and her baby up to 14 days after delivery only qualify for one fee.

Note that the visit has to be *requested and made* between 10 pm and 8 am.

If treatment can be given more effectively the GP can ask the patient to attend the surgery. For example, there may be a need to use medical equipment which is kept at the surgery.

GPs can 'pool' night visit cover between them or, with the approval of the FHSA, with other local practices. If, however, the GP uses a commercial deputising agency, the night visit fee is paid at a lower rate.

Sometimes the night visit is made to a patient who is only in the area for a few hours and is being treated as an emergency. If the night visit is made as an emergency treatment, then Form **FP-32** (in Scotland, **GP-32**; in Northern Ireland, **HS-14**) is used and the GP ticks a box to show that the visit was made at night.

You may need to check the form to make sure that the GP has listed all the patients seen at one location.

Vaccinations

For certain vaccinations and immunisations for patients aged 6 years and over, the GP can receive a fixed fee per treatment. The form to use is **FP-73** (in Scotland, **GP-73**; in Northern Ireland, **VAC**) and it is important to record whether the injection was a first dose, booster, etc., as this affects the level of payment made.

The fee is still payable if a member of the GP's staff (e.g. a practice nurse) administers the vaccination under the GP's direction.

Patients can be vaccinated by their GP if they are going abroad on holiday. Lists of vaccinations required by all the countries in the world are regularly updated in weekly publications such as *Pulse* or *GP* which are delivered free to most doctors' surgeries. These are normally pinned up in the GP's surgery.

Some vaccines are stocked and supplied by the surgery. In this case the GP can claim:

- The cost of the drug by sending up a form **FP-34-D** (invoice) (in Scotland, **GP-34-A** in Northern Ireland **HS-50**) to the Prescription Pricing Authority (PPA) (in Scotland, the Prescription Pricing Bureau; in Wales, the Welsh Prescribing Committee);

and

See also
Chapter 13
for patients
under the
age of 6
years

- The dispensing fee by sending an **FP-10** (prescription form) to the PPA (in Scotland, **FP-10**; in Northern Ireland, **HS-21**).

Child health surveillance (CHS)

A parent or guardian can ask a GP to look after the development and clinical well-being of their child. If a GP is on the CHS list (held by the FHSA) he or she can offer this service. For this the GP is paid a fee on a yearly basis and form **FP/CHS** (in Scotland, **GP/CHS2**; in Northern Ireland, **CHS**) is used for this.

To claim for CHS certain conditions have to be met:

- The child must be under 5 years of age.
- The GP must be either the child's own GP or a partner or associate of that GP.

Payments cease once the child reaches his or her 5th birthday. This is one reason why it is so important to record the patient's age correctly at registration.

Find out if your GP or one of his or her partners is registered for Child Health Surveillance.

ACCURACY

Finally, we would like to stress the importance of accuracy in filling in forms. Spelling and clear writing is particularly important. It is very easy for a reader to confuse, for example:

- The letter O and the number 0.
- The numbers 3 and 5 when written long-hand
- The numbers 9 and 7 when the circle of the 9 is not clearly drawn.

You can make a mistake all too easily when transcribing information from one sheet of paper to another, so try to find the time to double check.

Mistakes could mean lost income for the GP or interruptions from telephone calls from the FHSA trying to clear up problems with an incorrect form. Thus time taken to double-check is time well spent.

In this chapter you have learnt about the following FSHA forms used in general practice:

- FP-1　New patient registration.
- FP/RF　New patient examination.
- FP-19　Temporary registration.
- FP-24　Maternity services
- FP-1001　　Contraceptive care – ordinary service.
- FP-1002　　Contraceptive care – fitting an IUCD.
- FP-1003　　Contraceptive care – temporary resident.
- FP-81　Night visit.
- FP-73　Vaccinations (over 6 years old).
- CHS　Child health surveillance (under 5 years old).
- FP 32　Emergency treatment.

- FP-106 Immediately necessary treatment.

In addition you have learnt:

- The importance of accuracy when filling in forms.

APPENDIX 8a:

(Photocopy at 140% to achieve an A4 form))

Schedule of forms listed by form number

(see Appendix 8b for Forms listed alphabetically by item of service.)

Form Number:			Item of Service or Activity
England & Wales	Scotland	Northern Ireland	
FP-1	GP-1	HS-22	New patient registration
FP-10	FP-10	HS-21	Prescription pad
FP-13	not known	FP-13	Form given to persons completing service in HM forces
FP-19	GP-19	HS-15	Temporary patient registration
FP-24	GP-24	MMS1	Maternity services
FP-30	GP-30	FP-30	Order form for more forms
FP-32	GP-32	HS-14(E)	Emergency treatment
FP-34-D	GP-34A	HS-50	Invoice to Prescription Pricing Authority
FP-58	GP-58	HS-123	Baby's first registration card
FP-73	GP-73	VAC	Vaccinations (patients over 6 years old)
FP-81	GP-81	NV-1	Night visit
FP-82	GP-82	HS-128	Arrest of dental haemorrhage
FP-106	GP-105	HS-14(T)	Immediately necessary treatment
FP-1001	GP-102	FP-1001	Contraceptive care – ordinary service
FP-1002	GP-103	FP-1002	Contraceptive Care – IUCD fitted by GP
FP-1003	GP-104	FP-1003	Contraceptive care – temporary resident
FP/RF	GP/RF	RF	New patient examination
FP/CHS	GP/CHS	CHS	Child health surveillance

The GP Receptionist's Handbook
ISBN 0–7020–1834–1

Copyright © 1996 B.N.E. Quinn & P.P. Simons
Published by Baillière Tindall Ltd, London

APPENDIX 8b:
(Photocopy at 140% to achieve an A4 form)
Schedule of forms in order of item of service

Item of Service or Activity	Form Number: England & Wales	Scotland	Northern Ireland
Baby's first registration card	FP-58	GP-58	HS-123
Arrest of dental haemorrhage	FP-82	GP-82	HS-128
Child health surveillance	FP/CHS	GP/CHS	CHS
Contraceptive care – ordinary service	FP-1001	GP-102	FP-1001
Contraceptive care – temporary resident	FP-1003	GP-104	FP-1003
Contraceptive care – IUCD fitted by GP	FP-1002	GP-103	FP-1002
Emergency treatment	FP-32	GP-32	HS-14(E)
Form given to persons completing service in HM forces.	FP-13	not known	FP-13
Immediately necessary treatment	FP-106	GP-105	HS-14(T)
Invoice to Prescription Pricing Authority	FP-34-D	GP-34-A	HS-50
Maternity services	FP-24	GP-24	MMS1
New patient registration	FP-1	GP-1	HS-22
New patient examination	FP/RF	GP/RF	RF
Night visit	FP-81	GP-81	NV-1
Order form for more forms	FP-30		FP-30
Patient's medical card	FP-4	GP-4	HS-23
Prescription pad	FP-10	FP-10	HS-21
Temporary patient registration	FP-19	GP-19	HS-15
Vaccinations (patients over 6 years old)	FP-73	GP-73	VAC

The GP Receptionist's Handbook
ISBN 0–7020–1834–1

Medical Certificates and Reports

GPs don't only look after their patient's clinical needs. Their medical expertise, judgement and knowledge of their patients is frequently sought by others in order to verify the health status of individual patients.

To do this GPs fill in and sign certificates or reports, and they have a great responsibility to make sure that these certificates and reports are properly completed.

In this chapter you will learn about:

1) The certificates that you are most likely to deal with in general practice.

2) The reasons why these certificates are required.

3) The role the receptionist plays in the management of certificates within the practice.

Before you start – your practice should keep a schedule of fees for various certificates and reports. Find out where this schedule is kept in your surgery and refer to it as you read through this chapter.

INTRODUCTION

The doctor may issue certificates or reports either at the patient's request or at the request of another party. If the certificate or report is requested by someone other than the patient, the patient's consent is required.

Patients require certificates to confirm medical facts such as:

■ They are in good health and, say, fit to work, fit to travel or fit to drive.

or

■ They have some health problem and, say, are unfit to work, unfit to travel, should receive some compensation for an injury or claim on a health insurance policy.

or

■ Sometimes a summary of the patient's medical history is required by an insurance company when the patient applies for life or sickness insurance, or by a current or prospective employer.

For the doctor, there is much more to a certificate or report than a simple signature. The contents of certificates and reports can greatly affect the patient. They may stand to gain or lose financially. They may wish to be accepted as a normal risk by an insurance company, or they may want the Driver and Vehicle Licensing Authority (DVLA) to allow them to continue driving.

Because there is often a question of financial gain, any doctor signing a certificate or issuing a report will want to have a clear understanding of the relevant facts. Not to do so may create difficulties for either the patient or the doctor. For example, the patient may incorrectly be refused an allowance from the Department of Social Security (DSS). The doctor should ensure that the certificate is an honest statement of the available facts. In extreme circumstances, a careless signature, say on a private sickness insurance claim form, could lead to an accusation of conspiring with the patient to defraud the insurance company. The doctor must not place himself or herself in any jeopardy in signing a certificate.

When issuing any certificate, the doctor should make sure that he or she knows for what purpose the patient is going to use the certificate. For example, it has happened that a certificate declaring a patient unfit to travel on a bus tour was used by him to avoid travelling (by bus!) to attend Court in connection with an allegation of theft.

There are occasions when the doctor has to consider the well-being of the community above the interests of the patient. For example, when the doctor receives an enquiry from the medical officer at the DVLA, he or she should not hesitate to state the facts regarding the patient's medical condition, even if the patient's driving licence is likely to be withdrawn.

One other feature of certificates and reports is that not all certificates and reports are issued free of charge. The fee may be payable by the patient or by a third party such as an insurance company. You should familiarise yourself with the certificates that attract a fee and know how to find out the amount of the fee (see later in this chapter for some examples). Publications such as *Pulse* and *GP* carry tables of the recommended fees. Your doctors may have their own scale of fees. Practices often display their scale of fees for non-NHS services on the waiting room notice board. The doctors may adjust the fee payable by individual patients according to their circumstances.

Some patients resent paying any fee. Some will tell you that they thought the NHS covered all aspects of their medical care. However, completing certificates and reports takes up the doctor's time – a fee is quite reasonable. When the NHS doesn't cover the particular form the patient requires, you may need to explain this to the patient.

Some practices *pool* all fees earned; others pay the fee to the doctor who issued the certificate or report.

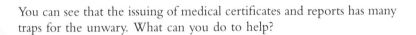

1) Find out where the schedule of fees for certificates and reports is kept in your surgery.

2) Find out what you should do with the fees you collect at the reception desk.

3) What should you do if the patient has no money with them to pay for a chargeable certificate or report?

You can see that the issuing of medical certificates and reports has many traps for the unwary. What can you do to help?

THE RECEPTIONIST'S ROLE IN MEDICAL CERTIFICATES

■ When the patient hands in the certificate for completion, you should collect as much information as possible. For certificates of incapacity to work (sick notes) and private sickness insurance claim forms, you should note what dates have to be covered on the certificate.

■ You should not promise that a certificate or report will be completed without question. The doctor may wish to discuss the matter with the patient.

- You should note the patient's day-time telephone number.

- If a fee is payable, you should tell the patient the amount that will be due.

- You should give the certificate, along with the patient's records, to the doctor.

PATIENTS' ACCESS TO REPORTS

The Access to Medical Reports Act 1988 gives the patient the right to see a report written by any doctor to an insurance company or to their current or prospective employer. The doctor must have provided clinical care to the patient at some time. The patient has the legal right to see the report before the doctor sends it to an insurance company or employer. The doctor may charge for allowing access to the report.

Find out what arrangements your practice has for a situation when a patient exercises his or her right under the Access to Medical Reports Act to view a report.

PATIENT'S CONSENT

One most important thing to note about certificates and reports is that, except in very particular circumstances, a doctor may not give out any information about a patient unless he or she has the patient's *informed* consent, which preferably should be in writing.

A copy of the patient's consent generally accompanies requests for reports from third parties such as insurance companies, solicitors, or the DSS.

SOME COMMON CERTIFICATES AND REPORTS

This section is not intended to cover every certificate and report you could possibly meet either now or in the future in general practice. However, by reading the following discussion of selected forms, you will hopefully devise some guidelines for managing the forms we do not mention.

SC-I

This form is used by the patient to self-certify a period of illness lasting between 4 and 7 days. Employers are required by law to accept these certificates.

No fee is payable.

Med-3

This is the common DSS 'sick note'. This is the DSS form most commonly used by the doctor to certify current or past inability to work due to illness. A Med-3 can be *open*, where it does not specify a return to work date, or it can be *closed*, where it does specify a date to return to work. A closed note must specify a return to work date within 2 weeks of the date of signing. Where a doctor knows that the patient is not likely to return to work at all, he may write that the patient is unfit to work until '*further notice*'.

A Med-3 form should not be issued without the doctor seeing the patient either on the day of issue or the previous day. The form cannot be issued retrospectively, although when a continuation Med-3 is issued just a few days late, the DSS will accept the statement '*unfit since* (date of expiry of previous note)' written in the space for comments on the Med-3. *The date of signing must always be the actual date of signing.*

If a Med-3 is lost, another one may be issued, but it should be clearly marked 'Duplicate'.

Sometimes the doctor might enter a vague diagnosis if he or she does not wish either the patient or any person who might see the certificate, e.g. an employer or a spouse, to know the exact diagnosis.

No fee is payable for a Med-3.

Med-4

This form was introduced in April 1995. When a patient has been off work due to illness for more than 28 weeks, the Benefits Agency will ask the GP to complete a one-off Med-4 certificate. The GP is asked to confirm the diagnosis and to provide 'fuller diagnostic and clinical information'.

Unless the patient is suffering from a severe medical condition, he or she will have to undergo an 'all work' test. If the patient is considered incapable of doing any work the GP will no longer have to issue certificates. On the other hand, if the Benefits Agency determines that the patient is capable of doing some work, then the doctor can appeal on the patient's behalf if their condition deteriorates or if the diagnosis changes.

No fee is payable.

Med-5

Form Med-5 is issued in the following circumstances:

■ If the doctor has not seen the patient but has received a letter from another doctor (typically a hospital doctor) within the preceding month indicating that the patient is not fit to work.

■ The patient has not been seen within the past 24 hours but the doctor feels able to issue a certificate of incapacity to work.

■ The patient returned to work without a closed certificate.

No fee is payable.

Regional Medical Service form RM-2

Form RM-2 is a form of enquiry about a patient receiving sickness benefit.

No fee is payable.

Private sick note

There is no special form for this. The practice may use headed note-paper, forms supplied by pharmaceutical companies or a specially designed form.

Some employers might require the patient to get a private medical sick note from the GP even though they have already submitted an SC-1.

The patient will have to pay a fee.

Private sickness insurance claim forms

Many patients insure themselves against illness in order to protect their income. Some policies may be connected to repayments on a mortgage or some other loan. If a patient becomes ill they can claim on these policies. The claim must include medical evidence of their inability to work. The patient must pay a fee to the doctor or practice.

Sometimes, the insurance company will write directly to the doctor. This is generally because they require more information. In this situation, the insurance company pays a fee directly to the doctor.

Private sickness policies generally exclude claims related to recurrences of conditions that existed or occurred *before* the policy's start date. Patients may not want the doctor to mention on the form that they have suffered from a similar illness in the past as to do so will almost certainly result in rejection of the claim. However, if the doctor accedes to this request, he or she could be accused of conspiring to defraud the insurance company.

Travel insurance claim forms

Patients travelling on holidays often take out travel insurance. If they claim on these policies for medical reasons they require medical evidence to support their claim. These certificates should be managed similarly to private sickness insurance claim forms. A fee is payable by either the patient or the insurance company.

Insurance enquiries

Insurance companies will require a report on a patient if he or she applies for life or permanent health insurance. These reports will include a summary of the patient's important past medical history and their current state of health, habits, and prescriptions. When these letters are received at the practice you should get the patient's medical records and give the records and the report request to the appropriate doctor. The insurance company pays a fee to the doctor.

Disabled Living Allowance

In certain circumstances, patients can apply for the Disabled Living Allowance (DLA). They may ask the GP to complete one of the pages at the back of the form. No fee is payable for this.

The DSS may write to the GP asking for further information. They will pay a fee for this.

In addition, if the claim for DLA is for a terminally ill patient who is expected to die within 6 months, the doctor may be asked by the patient, or more usually the carer, to send in a DS-1500. The DSS will pay a fee to the GP for completing the DS-1500.

Pre-employment medicals

As a last hurdle before their appointment to a new job, many patients have to undergo a medical examination. A fee is payable either by the patient or, more commonly, by the employer.

Employer's enquiries

After protracted periods of illness or following multiple short illnesses, employers may, with the patient's written consent, seek a report on the patient's condition and his prognosis. These reports are subject to the Access to Medical Reports Act. A fee is payable by the employer.

Fitness to drive

Patients aged over 70 years and others suffering from certain conditions such as diabetes or heart conditions may require either simple certification or examination and certification of their fitness to drive. A fee is payable, generally by the patient but sometimes by the insurance company.

Taxi and heavy goods vehicle drivers' medicals

Private hire drivers and LGV (large goods vehicles) and PCV (passenger carrying vehicles) drivers require regular medical examinations. A fee is payable either by the patient or by his or her employer.

DVLA reports

Drivers are obliged to report illness and disability to the DVLA who may then ask the GP for a medical report.

Infrequently, a DVLA enquiry may be generated by a Court appearance when a health problem is mentioned during a prosecution for a driving offence. A fee is payable by the DVLA.

Notifiable illness

Doctors are legally required to report or *notify* cases of certain infections. The doctor completes form Y-24 which is then sent to the medical officer for environmental health. Notifiable illnesses encountered in general practice include:

- Rubella (German measles).
- Acute meningitis.
- Scarlet fever.
- Measles.
- Mumps.
- Dysentery (amoebic or bacillary).
- Ophthalmia neonatorum.
- Food poisoning (actual or suspected).
- Infective jaundice.
- Viral jaundice.
- Whooping cough.

The doctor will receive a fee from the Health Authority.

Mat-B1

See Chapter 15 on maternity care.

Death certificates

This is one of the sad parts of the job. After a death, if the doctor is able to issue a death certificate, he seals it in an envelope specially provided for the purpose. The certificate is then given to the *informant*, who is usually a relative of the deceased.

Sometimes, the doctor will have to discuss the death with the coroner's officer. After the discussion the doctor may be willing to issue a death certificate.

The completed death certificate may be stored at the reception desk ready for collection by a member of the family.

No fee is payable.

Different forms are used to certify stillbirths and the deaths of live born children within the first 28 days of life. GPs are seldom required to certify these deaths.

Cremation forms (forms B, C and F)

If the cremation of a deceased patient is proposed, the funeral undertaker will ask the doctor to complete form B. Doctors often call this part of the form '*the first part*'. The doctor completing form B asks a second doctor to complete form C. Form C is often called '*the second part*'. The doctors completing forms B and C must not be in partnership and must not be related.

Both doctors receive a fee from the undertaker.

Fitness to travel

Insurance companies often ask elderly patients and others who declare a illness to provide a medical certificate that they are fit to travel.

The patient must pay a fee.

Orange badge applications

Patients whose ability to walk is restricted in some way may apply to the local Social Services for an *orange badge*. This provides them with special parking privileges.

A fee is payable by Social Services.

Pensions

Pension companies may ask their pensioners to obtain evidence to confirm that they are still alive. A statement of the fact must be signed by the doctor. This is to reduce or avoid fraud. The doctor should only sign the form if he actually knows the patient.

A fee is payable by the pension company.

Solicitors

Solicitors may request a report on a patient. You must make sure that you have the patient's consent for this report, as sometimes it is not completely clear whether the solicitor is acting for or against your patient.

A fee is always payable.

Some practices will not release reports to solicitors until the fee is paid. If prepayment is not the rule, then the practice should have some system for collecting outstanding fees.

Passport authentication

Doctors who are Commonwealth citizens and have known the patient for more than 2 years can sign passport forms confirming the patient's identity. The doctor must actually know the patient – it is not sufficient simply to have had the patient registered on the list for 2 years.

The patient pays a fee.

Freedom from infection/Certificates of health

Patients may require a certificate to confirm that they are free from infection or that they are fit to attend college or university or to engage in some activity.

The patient may have to pay a fee.

Exemption from jury service

Patients may be exempted from jury service for medical reasons.

A fee is payable by the patient.

Fitness to attend court

Patients may have to attend court as defendants or witnesses. A court hearing may have to be deferred for several months if a single witness cannot attend. A deferment is an expensive business for the court and the other witnesses. Certificates of unfitness to attend court must not be issued for trivial reasons.

Many people find giving evidence stressful and some may request a certificate excusing them from attending court because of the stress. Court officials are well aware that those unfamiliar with giving evidence find the experience anxiety provoking. Facilities for the support of stressed witnesses are available at most courts and should be considered as an option in the management of the stressed witness.

The patient will have to pay a fee for this certificate.

I) Find out where the following forms are kept:
  – SC-I,
  – Med-3,

      – Med-5,

      – notifiable illness forms,

      – DS-1500.

2) Ask your practice manager how you should handle requests for:

      – sick notes,

      – private insurance claim forms,

      – disabled living allowance (DLA) claims.

3) Find out what you should do when the practice receives a request for a report from someone other than the patient. For example:

      – an insurance company,

      – form RM-2 (from the Regional Medical Services),

      – a solicitor,

      – the DVLA,

      – the Social Services for an orange badge.

4) Find out who manages overdue fee payments.

5) Ask your manager what you should do when a funeral director wants one of your doctors to sign a cremation form.

6) Ask how you should handle a telephone call from a doctor in another practice asking for one of your doctors to complete a second part (of a cremation form).

7) Find out what you should do with a diabetic or elderly patient who requires a certificate of their fitness to drive.

8) What are your practice's arrangements for private medicals such as:

      – insurance medicals,

      – pre-employment medicals,

      – taxi and HGV driver medicals?

In this chapter you have learnt:

■ The most common kinds of certificates and reports the GP often provides to verify:

- the patient's illness or disability,

- the patient's level of health and/or ability,

- the patient's identity.

■ Important points to know about certificates:

- that some certificates require payment,

- which certificates require payment and by whom,

- the need to ask the patient's consent to release of information to a third party.

■ Why the GPs signature is not given lightly.

Drugs and Repeat Prescriptions

GPs can prescribe any drug passed by the Committee on Safety of Medicines for their patients.

However, they can only prescribe a limited amount of a drug at any one time, and drugs have a limited shelf-life. For this reason GPs can issue patients with repeat prescriptions and the practice receptionist has an important part to play in this.

In this chapter you will learn:

1) What a repeat prescription is.

2) How practices usually handle repeat prescriptions.

3) How repeat prescriptions are reviewed.

4) Other prescribing issues such as controlled drugs.

5) Sources of information about drugs.

At the end of this chapter you will find useful checklists which you can refer to at work, including a step by step checklist for dealing with repeat prescriptions.

Before you start – you may find it useful to obtain the following items:

- *MIMS* (*Monthly Index of Medical Specialties*).
- The *BNF* (*British National Formulary*)
- The *Drug Tariff*.
- Two FP-10s – one blank and one completed (or a photocopy of one).
- Two FP-10 (comp)s – one blank and one completed (or a photocopy of one).

INTRODUCTION

Before we look at how to deal with repeat prescriptions we will explain a few details about what a repeat prescription actually is. We will then explain a little about drug names and give sources of information about drugs that you will find useful or will need to consult. We describe the four main steps for issuing repeat prescriptions. A number of prescribing issues that you may encounter with drugs and repeat prescriptions are discussed. Finally, some other points related to drugs and repeat prescriptions are covered.

What is a prescription?

Many drugs that a patient needs cannot be bought freely over the counter at a chemist's shop. Instead the patient has to produce a prescription. This is a legal document signed by the doctor authorising the pharmacist to dispense the drugs to the patient.

What is a repeat prescription?

Briefly, a repeat prescription is a prescription issued for a drug that the patient has taken before. Most repeat prescriptions are for drugs a patient takes regularly. While the doctor may issue a repeat prescription during a consultation, most repeat prescriptions are issued without the doctor actually seeing the patient, in response to a request from the patient or their carer.

Patients may request repeat prescriptions for:

■ An illness that requires medication over a long period of time.

■ A recurring problem, such as hay fever in the summer.

■ An intermittent problem for which the patient requires an occasional prescription for a drug.

DRUG NAMES

Drugs usually have two names:

1) The **generic name** which is the drug's proper name.

2) The **proprietary name**, which is the name by which a drug is marketed by a pharmaceutical company.

If more than one company sells a particular drug it will have more than one proprietary name. For example, *paracetamol* is a generic drug name. *Calpol*, *Disprol* and *Panadol* are all examples of proprietary preparations containing paracetamol.

Currently, doctors are being encouraged to prescribe items by their generic names. This is because generic drugs are generally less expensive than their proprietary or *branded* equivalents. Some computer systems automatically ask whether a generic item should be substituted when a proprietary drug name is selected.

Many drugs can only be prescribed on NHS prescriptions by their generic name. In the *MIMS* (see below) these items are identified by the symbol G .

Find out if your doctors have any policy on generic prescribing.

SOURCES OF INFORMATION

If you have nursing experience or have previously worked in a pharmacy or doctor's surgery you may already know something about drugs. If you have not previously worked with drugs or prescriptions then you will need to know where you can find the information that you need. This information includes checking that a drug actually exists, whether it is available on the NHS, how the name is spelt, its various forms and typical dosage levels. Information about medicines should be readily available in the reception office. The common reference books are the *MIMS* and the *BNF*.

The MIMS

The *Monthly Index of Medical Specialties* (*MIMS*) is published monthly and posted to every general practitioner. There should a copy in every consulting room and several copies in the reception office.

It would not be uncommon to have previous months' editions of *MIMS* still in use in the practice. However, if you cannot find a particular drug in the index of an out-of-date edition, obtain the latest edition and try again.

We demonstrate the use of *MIMS* by looking up a sample drug – Ventolin (for bronchospasm), a commonly prescribed drug.

Look first at the *alphabetical index* at the back. Turn to the page listed. You should note the following:

- The heading at the top of the page says 'Bronchodilators and anti-inflammatories'. Drugs are grouped together in sections corresponding to their clinical application. You will sometimes find this useful.

- Looking at the entry for Ventolin, the entry tells us that it contains salbutamol. So Ventolin is a proprietary preparation containing the generic drug salbutamol.

- See that Ventolin comes in many forms, including tablets, syrup, sustained release tablets, inhalers,[1] rotacaps, ampoules for injection and nebules.

- Note that there is a separate dosage guide for each different form.

- Some forms are available in different strengths, e.g. the tablets come in 2 mg and 4 mg strengths. The strengths of liquid preparations are described in concentrations, e.g. the nebules come in 2.5 mg/2.5 ml and 5 mg/2.5 ml.

- Towards the end of the entry you will find the Special Precautions (**S/P**), Drug Interactions (**INT**), and known Adverse Drug Reactions (**ADR**).

Now look up salbutamol in the alphabetical index. The entry is shown in italic type in the index to tell us that this is a generic name. Several proprietary preparations that contain salbutamol are listed. Those with an asterisk (*) contain other active ingredients.

Find out what symbols are used in *MIMS* to identify the following classes of drugs:

- Prescription only medicines (POM).
- Drugs that may only be prescribed by their generic name.
- Controlled drugs.
- Items that may only be prescribed within the guidelines of the Advisory Committee on Borderline Substances.

[1] Inhalers, rotacaps, turbohalers, diskhalers and nebulisers are all different forms of inhaled drugs. Inhaled drugs are used in conditions such as asthma.

The *BNF*

Primarily aimed at prescribers, the *BNF* (*British National Formulary*) is still useful to the doctor's receptionist. Inside the front cover there is a brief section on how to use it and a list of the abbreviations and symbols used.

As well as more detailed information on drugs, it also contains several short chapters offering guidance on prescribing. The chapters on prescription writing and controlled drugs will be useful to receptionists. The other chapters in this section will provide useful background information to the receptionist.

Again taking Ventolin as an example, look this up in the index and turn to the page listed. The heading at the top of the page tells us that we are in Chapter 3: Respiratory System. The Ventolin preparations are listed under the name of the generic drug salbutamol.

For each drug there is a listing of:

■ Indications (the reasons why one might use the drug).
■ Cautions (conditions in which the drug should be avoided or used with caution).
■ Side-effects.
■ Doses (with a subentry for each different form of the drug).
■ The various preparations available.

The *Drug Tariff*

You should also be familiar with the *Drug Tariff*.

This book is published monthly and is distributed through the FHSA internal post to every GP. You will usually find the *MIMS* and the *BNF* more useful. However, the *Drug Tariff* does contain useful lists of:

■ General appliances.
■ Incontinence appliances.
■ Stoma appliances.
■ Borderline substances.
■ Drugs and other substances not to be prescribed on NHS prescriptions, the black list.

You will find a useful list of abbreviations relating to drugs and prescriptions in Appendix 10e at the end of this chapter.

PROVIDING REPEAT PRESCRIPTIONS

Practices generally have a procedure to allow patients to get repeat prescriptions without seeing the doctor. The typical system has five steps:

Step 1   The patient requests the repeat prescription.

Step 2   The practice staff prepare the prescriptions. This is generally done in batches.

Step 3   The doctor signs the repeat prescriptions, often after morning surgery.

Step 4   The prescriptions are filed, often near the reception desk, ready for the patients to collect them.

Step 5   The prescriptions are reviewed.

These steps are covered in more detail below:

Step 1 – The patient requests the repeat prescription

When taking a request for a repeat prescription always keep a careful note of the information the patient provides. Make sure you have a pencil and notepad ready.

Patients might order a prescription in any of several ways:

■ Many call to the reception desk requesting a prescription for what they need.

■ Many practices give patients *repeat prescription cards* which list the drugs they are allowed to have without seeing the doctor and provide a record of prescriptions issued. These cards are handed in by the patient and given back with the prepared prescription.

■ Patients sometimes bring in the labels from previous prescriptions. These are useful – keep these with your note of the request.

■ The working patient or the elderly patient might post a request for their repeat prescription. They may collect it later, or send a stamped addressed envelope (SAE) so that the prescription can be posted to them – make sure the request and the SAE do not get separated.

■ Some practices allow patients to telephone in their prescription requirements. When taking a request for a repeat prescription over the telephone be extra vigilant – it is much easier to make a mistake.

It can be helpful to ask the patient to spell out the name of the drug. It would be unwise to accept a request for '*Those blue tablets the doctor gave me last month*'.

Find out if your practice accepts requests for repeat prescriptions over the telephone.

When taking a request for a repeat prescription make sure that your note clearly identifies the patient, their age, and the prescription items they require. You should also note if the prescription is for a child, an elderly person, or a pregnant or breast-feeding woman. The checklist in Appendix 10a at the end of this chapter will help to remind you of these points.

You must take great care when taking requests for repeat prescriptions. Any mistake could seriously embarrass the practice. The wrong drug or the wrong dosage will endanger the patient, either by not adequately treating their condition or by making them very ill.

You must make sure that you get the names of the required drugs correct. Some drug names are very similar. For example **penicillin** and **penicillamine**. See Appendix 10b at the end of this chapter for a list of some more drugs with similar names.

Many drugs come in more than one form and in more than one strength. You must take great care to ensure that the patient receives the correct drug and in the correct strength. Most patients can tell how many times a day they take their medicine and many will also know the strength of the drug. Write these details down.

Find out how a patient can order his or her repeat prescription.

What should you do with the prescription request?

Step 2 – Producing prescriptions

NHS prescriptions are written on form FP-10 (in Northern Ireland, HS-21). The FP-10 (comp) is used for computer based repeat prescription systems. This is a larger form with a tear-off slip to the right of the prescription which is often used by the computer to print the patient's name and details of the prescription items. The practice can generally use some of the space on the slip to give information about practice services.

Prescriptions must be written in indelible ink or printed by a computer. Each must be dated and headed with

- The patient's name and address.
- If the patient is under 12 years of age you are legally required to specify the age in the appropriate box.

Several items may be prescribed on one form. Each prescription item must include the following details:

- The **name** of the drug.
- The **strength** (many drugs come in more than one strength).
- The **form** of the drug, e.g. 'tablets' or 'cream' (many drugs come in more than one form).
- The **dose**.
- The **frequency** of the dose.
- The **route** by which the drug is to be administered. Most drugs are taken by mouth (orally), but there are many other ways of giving drugs. See Appendix 10c at the end of this chapter.
- The **quantity** to be issued.

In most practices, the receptionists write out the prescriptions during the day. In many practices the receptionists use computers to print out prescriptions.

You should draw a line through any unused blank space on the prescription. When computers print prescriptions they generally strike through any unused space. This is to avoid an unscrupulous patient adding his or her own items.

Find and study some completed prescription forms. This will show you the style used by your own GPs.

Prescriptions printed by computers are generally recorded by the computer system. The computer can then print out a list of all prescriptions issued to the patient. Computerised systems can also search for all patients who have received particular drugs. This is useful when the doctors wish to track down patients who have had a particular drug, either for audit purposes or when there is any concern about the drug.

Any handwritten correction or alteration to a computer prescription must be initialled by the GP who first wrote the prescription. If the prescribing doctor is not available, which could easily happen if he or she was a temporary locum, then another doctor may initial the alteration, provided that he or she also signs the prescription.

A record must be kept of all prescription items issued. You will need to make a note in the patient's medical notes, either on a specific card or after the most recent entry in the clinical notes section.

Computers generally automatically keep a log of prescriptions issued. This log can be printed out if required.

Step 3 – The doctor signs the prescription

The prescription must be signed by a doctor. Doctors generally sign prescriptions at the end of the morning surgery.

Sometimes the doctor will not sign particular prescriptions. He or she might not be able to read your message, might not recognise the name of the drug required, the prescription might be deficient in some way, or the doctor might not be prepared to prescribe a particular drug without seeing the patient.

Ask your practice manager what you should do if the doctor declines to sign a prescription.

Step 4 – The patient collects the prescription

The prescription is then filed, probably somewhere near the reception desk, ready to give to the patient or their carer. Your practice may have a policy about who can collect a prescription, ideally it should *not* be someone under 16 years of age.

A prescription is valid for 13 weeks from the date of signing.

> **1)** Find out what happens to the signed prescriptions in your practice.
>
> **2)** Find out how you should record the issue of a prescription in a patient's records.

Step 5 – Periodic review of the patient

The GP will not issue repeat prescriptions of drugs without some periodic review of the patient to monitor their progress, perhaps to review the diagnosis and to re-evaluate their prescription.

Some practices permit the patient to have a fixed number of prescriptions before they must see the doctor for review; others insist that the patient be reviewed every so often, say, every 6 months. Computer systems are very effective at calculating when the patient should be reviewed and printing an appropriate message on the tear-off slip at the right time.

It can upset the patient if they are told they cannot have a repeat prescription without seeing the doctor. You may find it useful to say something like '*The doctor would like to see how you are getting on before prescribing further medicine*'.

> Find out the reviewing arrangements for patients receiving repeat prescriptions in your practice.

OTHER PRESCRIBING ISSUES

The 'black list'

In an effort to contain costs the Government has prohibited general practitioners from prescribing certain drugs. The list is popularly known as the black list. *MIMS* identifies black-listed drugs by using a special symbol – $\boxed{\text{X}}$.

Most black-listed drugs are available from the chemist without any form of prescription. The doctor can issue a private prescription if required for any black-listed item.

Incorrect or unclear prescriptions

From time to time, a patient will say that they did not receive what they ordered. Good problem management says that you should not get embroiled in a possibly heated discussion about what the patient did or did not order, but rather that you should find out exactly what is the problem and fix it. Where any problem was due to a lack of information or some inaccuracy in the patient's records, you should correct this straight away.

Pharmacists may ring the surgery to seek clarification of a prescription item or to point out some inconsistency in the prescription. These calls are important and you should make every effort to pass the call on to the doctor who wrote the prescription.

If the prescribing doctor is not available, see if another doctor is available who could help to resolve the issue. If the problem cannot be cleared up immediately, make sure the doctor is notified as soon as possible that there is a problem. Remember that *two* customers, the patient and the pharmacist, are being inconvenienced, so make every effort to fix the problem as quickly as possible.

Find out what you should do if a patient or a chemist queries a prescription.

Children

Always ensure that the doctor knows when a particular prescription is for a child. You could do this for example by writing the word child and the date of birth on the prescription request note or on the prescription itself. Children receive smaller doses of drugs. Very occasionally the dosage has be calculated from the child's weight and you may need to ask what this is.

Pregnancy

If you know or become aware that a patient requesting a repeat prescription is pregnant or breast-feeding, you should make sure the doctor knows this. Many drugs have the potential to harm the fetus or newborn child.

The terminally ill patient

Patients who are in the final stages of a serious illness such as cancer are generally taking large quantities of strong pain relieving drugs. They may also be prescribed other drugs to relieve troublesome symptoms such as coughs or vomiting. Sometimes they receive liquid dietary replacements. Often, and understandably so, the relatives of these patients are quite stressed.

The doctors may alter the prescriptions at short notice and, particularly with pain relieving drugs, the patient might need extra supplies at short notice.

Warfarin and other anti-coagulants

Anti-coagulants are drugs that slow the blood's normal clotting mechanism. A common anti-coagulant drug is **warfarin**. The dose of warfarin varies considerably between patients. To determine the correct dose of warfarin for them, the patient has to have a regular blood test. The test required is called the INR (International Normalised Ratio).

As soon as the result is available the hospital laboratory technician will generally telephone the surgery. If you receive such a call take careful note of:

- The identity of the patient.

- The INR result. This will consist of a number and a decimal, typically between 1.0 and 3.0.

See Chapter 11 where the INR is discussed in more detail

You should report the result to the appropriate doctor at the next convenient moment. Often the patient's dose of anti-coagulant will be altered according to the INR result and the doctor may issue an instruction regarding the amount of warfarin that the patient should receive.

- Find out how your practice handles and processes INR results.
- To which doctor should you give the report?
- How should you get a message to the patient about any change in their warfarin dosage?

Borderline substances

In certain conditions food products and toilet preparations have the merits of drugs, e.g. gluten-free bread for patients with coeliac disease, food supplements for debilitated patients, cosmetics for people with disfiguring skin conditions, or sun-blocking creams for people with photo-sensitivity. For patients with these conditions, products that are not generally considered as drugs may be prescribed on the FP-10.

The prescription item should be endorsed with the abbreviation *ACBS* to show that the prescription follows the advice of the Advisory Committee on Borderline Substances. Products in this category have the abbreviation 'ACBS' at the end of their entry in the *MIMS*.

A pharmacist may decline to dispense a borderline substance where the 'ACBS' endorsement has been omitted because the Prescription Pricing Authority may refuse to pay him for the item.

Look at the appendix on borderline substances in the *BNF*.

Urgent repeat prescriptions

Sometimes a patient will request a prescription and say that they cannot wait until the prescription is produced by the practice's routine repeat prescription system. This may be because they have allowed themselves to run short of tablets, they have mislaid their medicines, or they are flying to Tasmania tomorrow and can't wait for a routine repeat prescription.

Such a situation tends to provoke great irritation. However, good customer care and effective problem management can transform an unhappy disgruntled patient who is going to find another doctor when he or she gets back from Tasmania into a happy patient who leaves the surgery holding the required prescription having thanked the receptionist for looking after him or her so well. Each practice will have its own approach to this kind of problem.

Find out how your practice handles urgent requests for repeat prescriptions.

Hospital consultant's recommendations

When your patients are seen in hospital out-patient clinics the consultant will often give them a letter recommending treatment. This is not a prescription but merely a recommendation for the GP.

> ■ Find out how your practice handles these consultant recommendations.
>
> ■ Ask your practice manager what you should do if you cannot read the hospital doctor's handwriting.

Controlled drugs and drug addicts

Some drugs are subject to special regulations (The Misuse of Drugs Regulations 1985) (see Appendix 10d at the end of this chapter). These drugs are identified in the *MIMS* and *BNF* by the symbol CD (Controlled Drug). Prescriptions for controlled drugs must be completely written in the doctor's own handwriting – prescriptions printed off the computer or part-written by the receptionist are not acceptable. The form of the drug must always be specified, even if the drug concerned only comes in one form.

Narcotic analgesics, amphetamines and barbiturates are controlled drugs. Amphetamines are seldom prescribed nowadays. Barbiturates are used for epilepsy and there are still some patients taking them to promote sleep. Narcotic analgesics are prescribed to people in severe pain either on a short-term basis or for a more prolonged period, say, for a terminally ill patient.

Prescriptions for medicines containing **phenobarbitone sodium** may be written by the receptionist or printed by the computer, but the doctor must sign and date the prescription. (A computer might print the date on the prescription but the doctor must still handwrite it again.)

Addiction to narcotic analgesics is currently a major social problem. It is likely, especially if you are in an urban practice, that some of your young patients are misusing drugs. The doctor may be prescribing narcotics and other non-controlled drugs for them. In this case the doctor may order a controlled drug to be dispensed by instalments on a special form – FP-10-MDA. The amount of drug and interval between instalments (e.g. daily) must be stipulated on the prescription. No more than a 14-day supply of drugs may be prescribed on this special form.

Doctors are legally obliged under the Misuse of Drugs (Notifications of and Supply to Addicts) Regulations 1973 to send particulars of any known or suspected drug addict to the Chief Medical Officer at the Home Office. This must be done within 7 days of the patient's attendance. The list of drugs for which this regulation applies includes cocaine, barbiturates, and narcotic analgesics.

A drug addict is a person, who as a result of repeated administration of a drug, has become so dependent on it that he or she has an overpowering yearning for it to be continued.

Over-the-counter (OTC) drugs

Many different drugs are available over the counter, that is the patient can buy them without a doctor's prescription. More and more drugs are being designated as OTC. It may be cheaper for some patients who pay prescription charges to buy their medicines over the counter.

Medicines that can only be sold or dispensed when prescribed by a doctor are known as *prescription only medicines*.

Private prescriptions

When a prescription item is not available on the NHS or the drug is for exclusive use abroad, the doctor should issue a private prescription.

Some patients who were receiving NHS prescriptions for drugs that were later added to the 'black list' will continue to obtain private prescriptions for them.

NHS patients are allowed to obtain up to 3 months' supply of their *regular* medications for use abroad. However, private prescriptions must be issued for drugs such as anti-malarials and drugs the traveller wishes to have simply as a precaution against any travel-related illnesses such as traveller's diarrhoea and prickly heat.

The patient must pay a fee when a private prescription is issued.

Preparations purchased and dispensed by the practice

Some practices buy drugs, vaccines and other preparations which they then dispense to patients.

This is useful to the patients as they do not have to pay a prescription charge and they do not have to make a second appointment to come back to have the drug or vaccine injected.

It also helps the practice by enhancing its service to patients, by marginally reducing demand on appointments and by earning the practice a small amount of income for each item dispensed.

See also
Chapter 13
for more
details on
form FP-73

Very strict stock control is required. A prescription form (FP-10) and sometimes either an FP-73 or an FP-1001 is required for each item dispensed. Failure to fill out a prescription for a dispensed item will cost the price of that item which can be £5 for an influenza vaccine or £20 for a hepatitis A vaccine.

See also
Chapter 14
for more
details on
form
FP-1001

You should ask your practice manager what role you are expected to play in the management of this service. For example, your practice nurse might tell you that he or she has taken a Depo-Provera from stock and you might then be expected to fill out the required prescription form and get the patient to sign an FP-1001.

All the prescriptions for the various items dispensed by the practice are sent together at the end of the month, along with form FP-34-D, to the Prescription Pricing Authority.

Prescribing Budgets

All practices are set prescribing budgets by the FHSA. The doctors will wish to keep within their set budget. From time to time it may become practice policy to prescribe one particular branded preparation in preference to another. When the constituent drugs are identical this is a very effective way of reducing the cost of the drugs prescribed by the doctors without any detriment to the patient's care.

When such a policy is set in place, one of the doctors may prepare a letter to be given out to patients whose prescriptions have been altered.

> ■ *Mrs T. Efftees wants a repeat prescription for Thyroxine 150 mcg daily. Neo-Cytamen 1000 mcg injections (she gets one injection every 3 months).*
>
> *Get a blank FP-10 and write her prescription. Get your practice manager to check it for you.*

■ *Discuss the following scenario with your practice manager:*

It is Friday afternoon. The last surgery of the week has just started. You answer the telephone to Denise Coy. You know that her father is seriously ill with cancer of the pancreas. She tells you that the Macmillan Nurse visited her father earlier in the day and that she telephoned the GP who agreed to increase Mr Coy's dose of MST. She has just checked his tablet box and he doesn't have enough to last him over the weekend at the new dosage.

What do you think you might do?

In this chapter you have learnt:

■ What a repeat prescription is and what it is used for.

■ How to use the *MIMS* and the *BNF*.

■ The procedures for a repeat prescription:
   – taking the request,
   – producing the repeat prescription,
   – collecting the repeat prescription,
   – periodic review.

■ Other prescribing issues:
   – unclear prescriptions,
   – drugs for children,
   – drugs in pregnancy,
   – anti-coagulant therapy,
   – borderline substances (ACBS),
   – patients in a hurry,
   – hospital consultant's recommendations,
   – controlled drugs,

- private prescriptions,
- notification of drug addicts.

■ You have located:
- repeat prescription checklist, (Appendix 10a)
- similar sounding drug names, (Appendix 10b)
- drug administration routes, (Appendix 10c)
- prescription abbreviations, (Appendix 10e).

APPENDIX 10a
The request

Have a notepad and pencil ready. Basic details needed for the prescription request are:

— Patient's name.
— Age, especially if under 12 years.
— Elderly person (e.g. over 75 years)?
— Pregnant or breast-feeding woman?
— Check if a periodic review is needed for this patient.
— If a review is needed, suggest an appointment.

Filling out the repeat prescription

Use indelible ink for this task.

— Name of the drug (spell if necessary and ask what it is for).
— Strength.
— Form of drug, e.g. tablets or cream.
— Dose.
— Frequency.
— Allergies.
— Route.
— Quantity.
— Put the patient's age in box if they are under 12 years old.
— Draw a line through any unused space on the prescription.
— Handwritten alterations to a computer prescription must be initialled by the GP.

Updating the records

■ Record the details on the record, after the most recent medical entry

or

■ Record the details on special cards, if provided.

APPENDIX 10b
Similar sounding drug names

These drug names may sound similar but they do different things. Be careful.

Aldomet	Blood pressure
Alrheumat	Arthritis
Chlorpheniramine	Hay fever preparation
Chlorpropamide	Diabetic drug
Chlorthiazide	Diuretic
Chlormethiazole	Sedative
Danol	For gynaecological problems
Daonil	Diabetic drug
Denol	Bismuth for stomach troubles
Disopyramide	Heart drug
Dipyridamole	Anti-platelet
Gliclazide	Both used in diabetes
Glipizide	
Penicillin	Antibiotic
Penicillamine	Severe arthritis
Phenindione	Anti-coagulant
Phenindamine	Anti-histamine
Prondol	Anti-coagulant
Pindolol	Heart drug
Triptafen	Anti-depressant
Tryptophan	Anti-depressant

You should also be careful of the subtle changes to drug names used to denote the different strengths of a preparation. An example would include preparations containing the beta-blocker atenolol (generic name). Brand names include *Tenif, Tenoret 50, Tenoretic, Tenormin* (supplied in both 25 mg and 100 mg tablets) and *Tenormin LS*. Another example would be preparations containing the generic drug nifedipine. Brand names include *Adalat, Adalat LA* and *Adalat Retard*.

This list is not intended to be exhaustive but to illustrate the possible dangers associated with confusing similar drug names.

APPENDIX 10c
Routes by which drugs can be administered

- Oral.
- Injection:
    - intramuscular,
    - subcutaneous,
    - intravenous.
- Ear drops.
- Eye drops or ointment.
- Nose drops and nose sprays.
- Creams, lotions or gels for application to the skin.
- Inhaled.
- Rectally.
- Vaginally.

APPENDIX 10d
Common controlled drugs

- Barbiturate drugs (*Amytal, Seconal, Soneryl, Tuinal*).
- *Cyclimorph* (morphine).
- Diamorphine.
- *Fortral* (Pentazocine).
- Methadone (*Physeptone*).
- *MST Continus* (Morphine sulphate).
- *Omnopon* (Morphine HCl).
- *Temgesic* (Buprenorphine).

This list is not intended to be a complete list of Controlled Drugs but is meant for guidance only.

APPENDIX 10e
Prescription Abbreviations

These are abbreviations that are used extensively in writing prescriptions:

a.c.	before meals
Amps.	Ampoules
b.d.	twice daily
b.i.d.	twice daily
c.	with
Caps	capsules
Gtt	drops
Liq	solution
mitte	dispense (pronounced 'mittay')
mane	in the morning (pronounced 'mah-nay')
mcg	micrograms (there are 1000 mcg in one milligram)
mg	milligrams (there are 1000 mg in one gram)
Mist	mixture
ml	millilitres (there are 1000 ml in one litre)
nocte	at bed-time (pronounced 'nok-tay')
o.d.	once daily
o.m.	each morning
o.n.	each night
o.p.	original pack
p.c.	after meals
prn	as required
q.i.d.	four times daily
q.d.s.	four times daily
Rx	supply
Sig	let it be labelled
s.o.s.	when required
stat	to be taken immediately
Syr	Syrup
Tabs	tablets
t.d.s	three times daily
t.i.d.	three times daily
Ung	ointment
ut dict	as directed

SECTION III
SPECIFIC ACTIVITIES

11

Tests and Investigations

GPs can order tests for their patients either to help them decide what is wrong or to keep track of a patient's progress. Your role as a receptionist is to make sure that the process of arranging and reporting test results is as smooth as possible.

In this chapter you will learn:

1) The main types of tests used in general practice.

2) The importance of accuracy in completing request forms for tests.

3) Basic rules about handling and storing specimens.

4) How test results are dealt with by the practice.

5) The importance of confidentiality when dealing with test results.

You will also be able to consult a glossary of common tests used in general practice.

Before you start – your local pathology laboratory may publish a user guide, i.e. a directory of their services and telephone numbers. If so, find and browse through your practice's copy.

INTRODUCTION

Doctors perform tests and investigations on patients to help with the diagnosis or management of illness. For example, when presented with a pale, tired patient, the doctor might request a 'full blood count' (FBC) which reveals if the patient is anaemic. The same test will be done over the following months to monitor the patient's response to therapy.

Common examples of tests include:

- Examination of samples of body fluids such as blood and urine.
- Body tissue (e.g. moles excised by the doctor during a minor surgery session).
- x-Rays or scans.
- ECG (electrocardiogram) – test of the electrical activity of the heart.
- EEG (electroencephalogram) – test of the electrical activity of the brain.

Most tests are requested by the doctor in response to a particular clinical situation. Patients suffering from particular conditions or taking certain drugs have regular blood tests to monitor the condition or to measure the quantity or effect of a drug.

A common example of a condition requiring a regular blood test would be a patient with an underactive thyroid gland who takes the drug thyroxine. This patient would typically have an annual check of their thyroid function to make sure they were receiving an appropriate dose of thyroxine. Examples of drugs requiring regular blood tests would include warfarin and lithium.

Find out how you would find out which form to use for a particular test.

THE RECEPTIONIST'S ROLE IN MANAGING TESTS AND INVESTIGATIONS

The receptionist's role will vary from practice to practice, but typical involvement might include the following responsibilities:

- Maintaining adequate stocks (see Appendix 11c) of the items needed for common tests in the consulting rooms.
- Helping the doctors and nurses by filling out test request forms with the patient's details. The doctor or nurse will generally complete the clinical details and sign the request form.
- Helping patients to make appointments to get their tests done.

- Recording tests on the practice audit system.
- Helping to get the samples to the laboratory.
- Processing the many test reports received daily by the practice.
- Liaising with patients over results and any action required.
- Pursuing lost results.
- Pursuing urgent results.

HELPING THE PATIENT TO HAVE THEIR TEST

The doctor may do some tests during the consultation with the patient. For this reason, there must be an adequate stock of equipment in each consulting room (see Appendix 11c).

Alternatively, the doctor may send the patient to the reception desk to make an appointment for the test. This might be with the nurse or perhaps with the doctor himself or herself for another occasion when he or she would have more time. The patient may need to make a joint appointment with both the doctor and the nurse to have the test done. Some practices employ a phlebotomist – a person trained to take blood samples.

Find out who keeps the consulting rooms stocked with the items required for common tests. Are you expected to play any role in this? If so:

- Find out how you order the various stock items required for sample collection.

- Where are the sample bottles for ESR (erythrocyte sedimentation rate) and INR (International Normalised Ratio) tests kept?

X-RAYS AND SCANS

To have an x-ray or a scan, the patient will go to the local hospital. Sometimes the service will be available on a non-appointment basis – the patient takes a seat and waits (tell your patients to take a newspaper!).

Other investigations take a lot of time, e.g. special x-rays such as barium meals, barium enemas or cholecystograms. For these tests, the x-ray department will give the patient an appointment. Most hospitals have a phlebotomy clinic where the patient can have blood tests done.

Ask your manager how you should help patients who tell you that the doctor says they have to have the following tests:

- A blood test.
- A urine test for infection (urine culture and sensitivity (C&S)).
- A chest x-ray.

AUDITING TEST REQUESTS

Your practice may maintain a log or record of all tests requested by the practice. The practice manager may use this log to produce a summary report of all tests requested during the year. Also, it is useful to refer to this log when a test result goes missing.

Fundholding practices will have a particular interest in logging all tests done by the laboratory.

HANDLING SAMPLES

Hepatitis B (Hep B) or HIV (AIDS) infections present serious risks to health care workers.

Samples from patients *possibly* or *actually* infected with hepatitis B will generally have clear '*Hepatitis Risk*' stickers.

Samples from patients *possibly* or *actually* infected with HIV (AIDS) will also have clear warnings of the risk of infection. Very often, for reasons of confidentiality, a unique code for the patient will be used instead of their name on the request form and the specimen container.

The needles and syringes used to take blood samples probably present the greatest contamination risk to health care workers. All needles and syringes should be carefully disposed of in special *sharps bins*. Sharps bins are a hazard in themselves. They should never be placed where they might fall over – the flap does not always prevent the contents from spilling out. Also, small children have been known to stick their hands into them.

When full, these bins are permanently sealed and disposed of by specialist firms. *Sharps bins should never be allowed to become so full that they cannot be sealed without taking out some of the contents.*

To protect yourself:

■ Apply a plaster to any break in your skin, especially if it is on your hands.

■ Always put samples in the appropriate packaging, generally plastic bags, as soon as possible.

■ Always mop up any spillage. Wear disposable gloves and use disinfectant if necessary.

You should report any contamination by body fluid to your office manager who should note the details and investigate the incident.

■ Find out how the practice disposes of its sharps bins.

■ Discuss with your manager what special precautions you should take for samples from patients either *possibly or actually* infected with either hepatitis B (Hep B) or HIV (AIDS).

■ Find out how test samples from your practice are transported to the laboratory.

■ Find out how tests should be packaged for transfer to the laboratory.

GETTING TESTS TO THE LABORATORY

How your practice gets samples to the laboratory depends very much on how close you are to it.

Sometimes the patient will take their sample to the laboratory or take it to a local collection point.

A delivery service may have been set up by the FHSA or the laboratory. A collector might call once or twice daily to the practice, collecting samples and bringing back test results. The same service might provide an internal mail service and bring supplies from various sources such as the FHSA.

Rural areas may need to depend on the general post. The Post Office has strict regulations about how carefully tests must be packaged.

Samples kept on practice premises awaiting transfer to the laboratory must be stored in a cool place. Samples deteriorate over time, especially in warm places. You should not leave samples on a window sill or near a radiator. If a sample needs to be kept for a prolonged period you should store it in a fridge.

GETTING TEST RESULTS BACK

The laboratory normally sends the test result to the practice through the internal post service, if available, or the general post.

In recent years, various regions have set up electronic links where a computer in the practice connects with the laboratory's computer. Such links offer speedy transfer of test results. Electronic links will probably become more commonplace.

When the laboratory technician sees a very abnormal test result, he or she will often telephone the practice with the result. When this happens, you should pass the message to the appropriate doctor. You should also extract the patient's records from the files and note their record and telephone number ready for the doctor.

Your laboratory may telephone all INR results. These are not necessarily abnormal results, but will require an assessment by the doctor and a decision on what dose of warfarin a patient should take until the next INR test is done.

What should you do when a laboratory technician telephones and wants to speak to the GP?

The laboratory will send the result of any test to the doctor who ordered the test in the first place. Patients who have tests done in an out-patient clinic may expect the practice to have the result within a few days. The practice will often not find out the test result until the hospital doctor writes with his or her report. If your doctor wants to know the result then you can either telephone the consultant's secretary or telephone the laboratory direct and ask for a copy of the test report. If a test is significantly abnormal, the hospital doctor will generally telephone the practice with the result.

Unfortunately, tests and test results can go astray. Forms might not be correctly completed, the handwriting may be hard to read and a clerk at the laboratory may guess the surname wrongly, or the same clerk might mistype an entry on a computer so that the result is sent to the wrong practice. Specimen tubes can break in transit or in the laboratory. A test result could be misfiled in another patient's file. If a test result is overdue, you may have to contact the laboratory (see below).

- Find out how test results are processed within your practice.
- Do *all* doctors see *all* results or do the doctors only see results of tests they have personally ordered?

PROCESSING TEST RESULTS WITHIN THE PRACTICE

When the test result is received by the practice the doctor needs to see it. The doctor may direct that a particular course of action is required. After this the test result should be filed safely in the patient's notes.

Test results may be *normal* or *abnormal*. *Normal* results often simply get filed in the patient's record. *Abnormal* results may require some action. The action required will depend on the degree of abnormality.

Sometimes the result will still simply get filed. Sometimes the doctor will want the patient to make an appointment to discuss the test result or to have further tests. Less commonly, the doctor may have to contact the patient urgently and either institute or alter treatment, or admit the patient to hospital.

Even *normal* test results may prompt further action. The doctor might have expected the test to produce an *abnormal* result to confirm a postulated diagnosis. He or she may have to think again about the patient's symptoms and the clinical findings if the test does not support the diagnosis.

Many practices use a stamp that summarises the action options. A simple stamp might look like this:

Normal	
To make appointment	
Repeat test	
To pick up prescription	

If your practice uses such a stamp, then you should stamp each test result on receipt. When doing this, you must take care not to overstamp some important detail such as the patient's details or the test result.

The doctor will then put a tick against the appropriate line. The doctor may also write a simple message on the result to be given to the patient when they telephone for the result.

■ When a test result suggests that some action is required, say a patient needs a prescription, how is this organised in your practice?

■ Find out how your laboratory identifies abnormal results. Computerised laboratories often mark abnormal results in a special way. For example, the computer might print one or more asterisks (*) against an abnormal result.

■ Find out what your practice does with abnormal results.

GETTING TEST RESULTS TO PATIENTS

Generally, the patient will telephone to see if their test is back. The patient will want to know if the test is normal and, if not, what action is required. The action might be something the patient has to do, such as stick to a diet or simply have the test repeated after an interval. Or, the doctor may have to take some action such as prescribe a drug or refer the patient to a specialist.

As always, you must know to whom you are talking. Make sure that you know to which Mary Jones or which Henry Rheinhart – the 47-year-old father or his 16-year-old son – you are speaking.

A patient having several different blood tests does not need to have a separate needle stab for each one. Several different tests can be done on one blood sample provided that sufficient blood is taken and divided appropriately between the required specimen tubes. You should check with the patient how many different tests were done. If they do not know you may have to check in their records. You could tell a patient that his or her tests were normal but the next day another test done from the same needle stab could return with an abnormal result. Suppose the patient does not contact the practice again for months because he or she thinks there is nothing to worry about and the abnormal result gets filed or overlooked. You could appreciate the doctor's embarrassment when the patient attends some time later saying he or she still feels ill and the doctor finds the overlooked test result in the record folder.

Patients may ask whether a hospital report or a test result has arrived before they make an appointment. In these cases, you should make sure the required report or result is available in the patient's record when they see the doctor.

Some patients take a particular interest in their test results. Some are not satisfied simply to be told that their test is normal or abnormal and might want to know the actual test result. This is to be encouraged. These patients are involved in the management of their medical problem. Generally these patients do better than those who are not interested in their problems.

Never forget that abnormal tests are sometimes an improvement on a previous test result. A patient with jaundice will have abnormal liver function tests. As the jaundice and the liver problem subsides, their liver function tests might still be abnormal, but compared with previous results of, say, 2 weeks earlier it will be seen that the problem is actually getting better. As another example, a haemoglobin of 9.5 g/dl is abnormal but would represent an improvement on a previous result of 8.2 g/dl.

Always remember that a test might be normal but the patient might not be feeling any better. Never simply give out a test result and move quickly on to the next telephone call. Listen to what the patient is saying to you. You might hear disappointment in their voice. If you pick up any clue that the patient is not entirely happy, especially when giving out a normal result, you could ask how they are. If they say that they are not a great deal better or they are still troubled by their symptoms then you should offer to make them an appointment to see the doctor.

Discuss the following situation with your manager. A urine C&S shows that the bug causing a patient's urinary tract infection is resistant to the antibiotic prescribed by the doctor. How is this situation managed in the practice?

Remember it is the patient who is treated, not test results.

CONTACTING THE LABORATORY

You may need to contact the laboratory when results are required urgently or if a result seems to have gone missing. Laboratories tend to be large places with many technical and clerical staff. They are generally divided into sections such as haematology, biochemistry, microbiology and histology:

■ **Haematology** is concerned with the cells of the blood and the mechanisms of blood clotting.

- **Biochemistry** is to do with the levels of various chemicals in the blood. Particular chemicals might ordinarily be present in blood but their levels may be abnormally low, within a normal range or abnormally high.
- **Histology** is the study of tissue. It is used to detect abnormalities such as cancerous changes in biopsy samples.
- **Microbiology** is concerned with the identification and control of the bacteria and viruses that cause infection in humans.

You need to know which section to contact for each particular test. If the laboratory publishes a 'user guide', it will generally have a list of telephone numbers. Some laboratories print their telephone numbers on their request forms.

Before you telephone the laboratory, you should collect as much information as possible such as:

- the patient's name,
- the patient's date of birth,
- what test(s) were done, and
- the date of the request.

Make sure you have a pen and paper handy to note down the results. Alternatively, you might ask if the result could be faxed to the practice. If the laboratory has no record of the test, you must arrange for it to be repeated.

Make a photocopy of the blank table in Appendix 11b at the end of this chapter. Now fill in the details of your own local laboratory's forms and test result delays. You can then refer to it when necessary. Advancing technology in laboratory equipment and communications is reducing the interval in between sending the test to the Laboratory and receiving the result. Because of this, you may need to review your table periodically.

You may need several copies because you may be getting the same tests done by more than one hospital or laboratory.

In this chapter you learnt:

■ The different types of test normally requested by GPs.

■ How to get samples to the laboratory.

■ Communications between the hospital or laboratory and the practice.

■ How to communicate test results to the patient.

APPENDIX 11a
Glossary of common tests

This glossary is not meant to be a comprehensive review of every test and investigation currently available. The laboratory department normally responsible for the test is shown in brackets.

Blood tests

Full blood count (FBC) (*haematology*) – this is a common test. It shows if the patient is anaemic. It also gives the white cell count. Certain abnormalities can suggest alcohol abuse or thyroid disease.

Patients taking certain drugs, e.g. carbimazole and salazopyrin, must have regular white cell counts.

Erythrocyte sedimentation rate (ESR) and **Plasma viscosity (new test)** (*haematology*) – these tests give a non-specific indication of inflammation. They can be abnormal in infections and in inflammatory conditions such as arthritis and cancers.

Serum iron and total iron binding capacity (TIBC), vitamin B$_{12}$ and folic acid (*haematology*) – these tests are done when certain abnormalities are picked up on the full blood count. They help the doctor accurately to diagnose the deficiency that caused the patient's anaemia.

International normalised ratio (INR) (*haematology*) – this is used for the management of patients on anticoagulants such as warfarin. The INR is discussed in the *BNF* (Section 2.8.2).

Urea and electrolytes (U&Es) (± creatinine) (*biochemistry*) – this is used in the management of kidney conditions. It is also used to monitor patients on diuretics (water pills). One electrolyte is potassium. Many laboratories will only measure potassium levels on fresh blood samples. Potassium levels in blood samples that are even one day old are inaccurate. Your practice may have a policy of only taking blood for U&Es in the morning.

Liver function tests (LFTs). Chemispek Profiles (*biochemistry*) – these closely related tests measure several different enzymes and body salts and are used in a variety of clinical situations.

Cardiac enzymes (*biochemistry*) – this is used in the diagnosis of heart attacks.

Blood sugar (*biochemistry*) – this is used in the diagnosis and management of diabetes.

Glycosylated haemoglobin (HbA1) (*biochemistry*) – this is used in the management of patients with diabetes.

Cholesterol and lipid profiles (*biochemistry*) – patients may have their cholesterol levels checked as a screening test or as part of the management of known cholesterol problems. A high blood cholesterol is known as hyper-cholesterolaemia.

Thyroid function test (TFT) (*biochemistry*) – this is used to diagnose and manage thyroid disease. An underactive thyroid (hypothyroidism/ myxoedema) is quite common. You will see many patients receiving prescriptions for thyroxine (replacement therapy for the thyroxine they are not producing for themselves). These patients will typically have their TFT checked annually.

Serum lithium (*biochemistry*) – patients taking lithium salts (proprietary name Priadel) must have a blood test every 3 months to measure the level of lithium in their blood.

Other blood tests – these include:
- measurements of other hormone levels,
- serum electrophoresis, and
- screening for drug abuse.

Urine culture and sensitivity (MSSU C&S) (*microbiology*)

When a doctor suspects that a patient is suffering from a urinary tract infection, they will request a mid-stream sample of urine (MSSU) for culture and sensitivity (C&S). This test might also be requested to ensure that an infection has been treated successfully.

The sample is sent to the laboratory where it is incubated. Any infection detected is tested against antibiotics. If the test shows infection, the laboratory will recommend which antibiotics the patient should or should not have.

If the organism (bug) causing the infection can be killed by a particular antibiotic, it is said to be *sensitive* to the antibiotic. If the antibiotic has no effect on the organism, then the organism is said to be *resistant* to the antibiotic.

There is no point in giving the patient a prescription for an antibiotic to which the organism is resistant. The doctor will want to give an antibiotic shown to be effective against the organism. Often the doctor will have already started the patient on an antibiotic. If the urine C&S test shows that the antibiotic is ineffective, the doctor will want to change the prescription.

Urine *Stix* testing for glucose and/or albumin – these are simple screening tests done in the surgery to detect glucose or albumin in the urine (glycosuria or albuminuria).

Glycosuria is an important finding which can suggest that the patient is diabetic. Glycosuria can occur in pregnant women who are not diabetic.

Albuminuria can be a sign of some problem with the kidneys or bladder.

Urine testing for albumin and glucose is a requirement for many insurance and occupational medical examinations. It is also a routine part of ante-natal care.

Pregnancy tests (*varies*) – a sample of the patient's urine is tested at the Laboratory.

Semen analysis (*histology*)
This is done both after a vasectomy and in the investigation of infertility.

Cervical cytology (*histology*)
This is discussed in the Chapter 14.

Faeces C&S and vaginal swabs (*microbiology*)
These tests are used to find out if the patient has an infection. The samples are incubated and managed similarly to urine C&S tests.

x-Rays and ultrasound scans
x-Rays can be plain films or can involve the administration of a radio-opaque dye. A chest x-ray is a common example of a plain film type of x-ray.

Examples of x-rays involving radio-opaque dyes include barium swallows, barium meals, barium enemas, cholecystograms and intravenous pyelograms.

A barium meal is an x-ray of the oesophagus (gullet), stomach and the first part of the small intestine. The patient is given a drink containing the radio-opaque barium. A barium swallow is used to look at the oesophagus.

A barium enema is an x-ray of the bowels. The barium is administered as an enema.

A cholecystogram (Graham's test) is an x-ray of the gallbladder. The patient is given the dye orally.

The intravenous pyelogram (IVP) involves injection of the dye into a vein. This x-ray illustrates the kidneys, ureters and bladder.

Ultrasound scans are another way of looking at body parts such as the kidneys, the bladder, the pancreas and the genital organs. Ultrasound uses sound at high frequencies to create an image on a screen.

Electrocardiograph (*ECG*)
The ECG shows the electrical activity of the heart.

An ECG machine is required, along with someone who knows how to use it. Your practice may have a machine and your practice nurse may have been trained in its usage. If the practice does not have a machine, the patient should make an appointment to have the test at the local hospital.

APPENDIX 11b
Local laboratory details
(Photocopy at 140% to achieve an A4 form)

Laboratory name:				
Test	Form	Container	Result in ? days	Laboratory section

NOTES:
(Days not to send results/latest time for tests)

The GP Receptionist's Handbook
ISBN 0–7020–1834–1

APPENDIX 11c
List of items needed in the consulting rooms for tests

■ Test request forms:
  - haematology,
  - biochemistry,
  - microbiology,
  - histology,
  - x-ray,
  - ultrasound.

■ Syringes:
  - 1 ml,
  - 2.5 ml,
  - 5 ml,
  - 10 ml,
  - 20 ml,
  - 30 ml.

■ Needles:
  - green (most commonly used for blood sampling),
  - blue (used for injections and occasionally for blood sampling), and
  - orange (used only for injections).

■ Sharps bins – for the safe disposal of syringes, needles, glass injection ampoules and other sharp objects.

■ Sample bottles:
  - red topped tubes (known as EDTA bottles),
  - orange topped heparin tubes,
  - white topped 'serum Z' tubes,
  - yellow topped tubes (for blood sugar tests),
  - ESR tubes, and   these are kept refrigerated
  - INR/clotting studies tubes.

■ Alcohol pre-injection swabs.

■ Cotton wool.

■ Plasters.

■ Swabs.

■ KY Jelly.

- Vaginal speculums – these should be easily available. It might not be practical to keep speculums in each room.

- Surgical gloves.

- Equipment for cervical smears:
    - glass slides,
    - pencil (with sharpener),
    - Ayre's spatulae (or whatever device the practice uses),
    - fixative,
    - transport boxes for the glass slides.

12

Emergencies

Although most of your work will be routine, you will occasionally have to deal with an emergency of some sort. Each practice has its own way of responding to emergencies and this chapter offers a few points of guidance which will help you to prepare for these situations.

In this chapter you will learn:

1) How to find out the nature of the problem from a distressed caller

2) The main options available to you for dealing with the problem

3) The importance of learning how to handle emergencies through the experiences of yourself and others.

4) Your own practice's policies for dealing with a number of typical scenarios.

Before you start – find out where the various telephone numbers and emergency rosters are kept in your practice.

INTRODUCTION

Most of the contact you will have with patients will concern routine requests for appointments, repeat prescriptions, sick notes and so on. However, some patients will get seriously ill, sometimes suddenly. They or their relatives will contact the practice looking for urgent assistance. Most of them will use the telephone, although there is nothing to stop people running in to the reception desk.

We are going to discuss how you should manage these calls. It is unlikely that you will be allowed or expected to handle these urgent calls until you have had some training in their management. The training will probably include some discussion with your manager, observing more experienced colleagues and handling urgent calls under supervision. There is no absolutely right or wrong way of handling emergencies and the only real teacher is experience. However, the basic points outlined in this chapter will help you.

In your early days in the practice you should observe how your more established colleagues manage urgent calls. Afterwards, when the drama has settled down you should ask your colleague what had happened to the patient and why they did whatever they did. We have included at the end of this chapter a number of scenarios for you to work through and discuss with your practice manager.

BASIC MANAGEMENT FRAMEWORK

You need to have a basic management framework in order to be able to get the most information from the caller as efficiently as possible. You must *take control of the conversation* and keep control until you have collected the required information.

You can take control of the conversation by asking questions. When handling an urgent call you should keep your questions short. Never ask two questions at once. For example, don't ask '*What is your name and date of birth?*'. Instead ask for the person's name first, and then ask for their date of birth.

It can be very stressful to manage an urgent call. The person making the call will often be very distressed. They might be tearful. Or, they might talk very quickly, telling you only that there is a major problem with some-one somewhere, and demanding that a doctor be sent immediately. You might worry about doing the wrong thing and being held responsible for a worsening of the patient's condition. Urgent requests for medical assis-tance generally come in on the telephone, making it very much a one-to-one situation. Any stress in the caller's manner will often aggravate your own stress.

Some people talk very fast when they are stressed or excited. A useful tactic to *slow things down* is to repeat back to them what they have said but at a noticeably slower pace. This:

- Increases your control of the conversation,
- Provides you with more time to make notes of whatever the caller is telling you, and
- *reassures the caller that you are listening and responding.*

In case the telephone call is cut off for any reason, *take the caller's telephone number* very early in the conversation. Technology now makes it possible to obtain the telephone number of people who telephone you. If your telephone is on a digital exchange you simply dial the number **1471** after the caller has hung up. A computerized voice then tells you the telephone number of the caller. This facility may not work if your practice has several lines all using the same telephone number.

Find out if the practice telephone system allows you to obtain the telephone number of the last caller and try it out yourself on the next incoming call to the practice.

Be wary of answering any questions until you have got the basic information. For example, before you have written down the patient's name and address, the caller might ask '*Will you send the doctor?*'. You might answer '*Yes*' and before you know what is happening the caller says '*Thanks*' and hangs up the telephone, leaving you without any means of contacting the caller again. You might handle questions by saying something like '*First let me get the patient's name and address*'.

You must find out:

- the patient's name,
- the patient's age,
- where the patient is, and
- a brief description of what has happened.

If the problem involves *pain*, then ask where the pain is. Try to get an indication of how much distress the patient is in. Pain cannot be measured and you will only receive an emotive description of the patient's condition.

If the patient is *bleeding*, you must establish:

- where they are bleeding from,
- how much they are bleeding, and
- if they are still bleeding.

Measuring the amount of blood lost is difficult, but do ask the caller to estimate the amount of blood. You might ask them '*Is it a tablespoonful or a cupful?*'. The more blood there is, the more urgent the situation.

If the patient has suffered a head injury, find out if they have been unconscious. Any suggestion of unconsciousness is important.

If possible you should ask

 — When did it happen?

 — Has this ever happened before?

 — Does the patient suffer from any major illnesses?

 — With whom is the patient registered?

If your practice is computerised, you could quickly answer the last question for yourself. Write down as much as possible.

It can be quite difficult to get the required information if the caller is very distressed or excited. Some people are irritated by the questions. However, you must make sure you get the required information. You should watch how your more established colleagues handle this sort of situation. When faced with an irritated, stressed caller you could ask '*Could you just quickly tell me* . . . '. You will develop your own style in time.

A checklist of information that you must collect in an emergency is given in Appendix 12a at the end of this chapter.

OPTIONS FOR MANAGEMENT

Having collected some information on the patient's problem you are then faced with the question of what to do next. As you become more experienced you will have a better idea of what the practice expects you to do. In your early days, you should think about what you think you should do and then discuss the patient's problem and your proposed plan with a more senior member of staff, say your practice manager. Thinking about what you should do *before* discussing the case with your manager will help you to develop self-sufficiency. If one of your doctors is on the premises then obviously you can approach him or her with the patient's problem.

What you do in any situation depends on the nature of the problem, how easily you can contact the duty doctor and your assessment of the degree of urgency. Your practice may have a list of crisis situations which are referred immediately to hospital. Your practice manager will discuss this topic with you during your training.

Your options for action include those described below.

Request an urgent ambulance

In certain circumstances it will be more expedient for the patient's care for you to call an urgent ambulance to take the patient straight to hospital. Examples might include the following situations:

- An elderly lady has fallen and is now unable to bear weight on one leg.
- A 50-year-old man suddenly complained of unpleasant central chest pain, looked very uncomfortable and collapsed.
- A teenager has been found in an unconscious state and there are several empty tablet bottles lying nearby.

Accident & Emergency Department

You may advise the patient to go to the Accident & Emergency Department at the nearest hospital. Examples of patients you might advise in this way are:

- A boy who has fallen off a playground swing and now cannot use his arm.
- A toddler who is believed to have swallowed a coin.
- A child who has been playing with granny's tablets and who may have swallowed some of them.

Arrange an urgent home visit

In this case, you contact the duty doctor and tell them the details of the urgent call.

Arrange an urgent appointment

In certain circumstances the patient may not be ill enough to require a home visit. In these situations the patient could be seen in the surgery.

Arrange a less urgent/routine appointment or home visit

Sometimes, the urgent call might not require any urgent action. When the doctor hears the story and perhaps speaks with the patient, he or she may decide to make a more routine appointment to see the patient either in the surgery or at their home.

- The 'hot ill child' is a common urgent call. Find out how the practice manager expects you to handle this situation.
- Find out if your doctors suture wounds.

Contacting the doctor

In a group practice, the doctors often take it in turn to be on duty for urgent cases that arise during the working day. This is not the same as being on-call for emergencies at night and at weekends. You should check the duty roster carefully.

If the duty doctor is on the premises then you should tell him or her straight away about the urgent call while you still have the caller on the telephone.

Get the patient's medical records for the doctor. If your practice is computerised, you might instruct the computer to print out details of recent consultations, past medical history and current medication. You should know how to find details of recent consultations, recent hospital reports and details of important past history. If you have to telephone the doctor, he or she may ask you to read recent details from the notes.

If the duty doctor is not on the premises, you should contact him or her. Some doctors have radiopagers while an increasing number have mobile telephones. Your practice may have procedures for contacting the doctors. For example, perhaps you should always try their home telephone number first and then their mobile telephone.

You should know what to do if you cannot contact the duty doctor. This can happen very easily. They might not be able to get to a telephone to answer their radiopager or the battery in their mobile telephone may be flat. You could contact one of the other doctors. You could leave messages for the doctor at various places you know he or she is visiting.

If the doctor has to leave the surgery during a consulting session or if he or she is late starting a surgery, you will have to explain to patients why the surgery is running behind schedule and apologise. Options you can offer patients include: waiting until the doctor can see them, letting them leave to attend to some other business and return a little later, or making them another appointment to see the doctor. In a group practice, other doctors may be able to see some of the patients.

- Find out how to tell which doctor is on call
- Find out how to contact the duty doctor.

'He's getting worse'

Sometimes the caller will telephone again to tell you that the patient's condition has deteriorated further. When this happens you must reconsider your options. The appropriate action will depend totally on the given situation. Training in urgent calls, supervised urgent call management and, eventually, your own experience will guide you.

URGENT CALLS FROM PATIENTS NOT REGISTERED WITH THE PRACTICE

From time to time your doctors will be asked to give assistance to people not registered on their list. You should ensure that the appropriate form is signed: FP-19 (temporary resident), FP-32 (emergency treatment), or FP-106 (Immediately necessary treatment).

See also Chapter 8 on FHSA forms

- Ask your practice manager what you should do if an acutely ill person is not registered with your practice.
- Find out where forms FP-32 and FP-106 are kept. Obtain one of each and ask your manager to tell you how you should fill them in.

POINTS TO REMEMBER

1)   Make sure you know at the start of every shift which doctor is on-call for emergencies that day. Write their name on a 'Post-it' note and put it up in a place where you can easily see it.

2)   Reassure the caller that you are treating their call as an emergency.

3)   Know your options.

4)   Explain *why* you need the basic details.

5)   Get the details correct – it is all too easy to send the doctor to the wrong address or provide the wrong set of notes. Check the details back with the caller before hanging up.

Consider the following scenarios. Make some notes on questions you would like to ask, decide what you would do, and then discuss your plan with your practice manager.

If the practice manager's advice is different from what you had in mind, it provides you with an ideal discussion point. You should ask why they advised you in a particular way and what problem they see with your approach.

- Mrs Smith rings to say that she is very worried about Abigail who has been 'unwell' all day. She is very hot and has a rash.

- Sarah Morgan tells you her 76-year-old father has just vomited a lot of blood. He now feels quite unwell and has had to lie down on his bed.

- Mrs Jones telephones. She is very upset. Her son Thomas, aged 15 years, was fixing a puncture on his bicycle when he just collapsed, jerked several times and now he is just lying there on the ground.

- Mrs Patel telephones to say that her little girl has fallen off her bicycle. She has a nasty gash on her leg that is bleeding a lot.

- A Home Help telephones to say that she has just arrived at Mrs O'Brien's house to find her lying on the floor in the kitchen. She has a nasty bump on the head. The

Home Help tried to help Mrs O'Brien stand up but she shouted out with pain from her left leg.

- Mrs Tanger telephones. She needs the doctor to see her 68-year-old father straight away. Her father lives alone. One of her father's neighbours found him wandering in the street wearing only his pyjamas.

- Mr Davies telephones to say that his 4-year-old son has just fallen off a climbing frame and banged his head on one of the lower poles. He has been sick and is now lying down.

- You answer the telephone to Mrs Cox. She tells you that her husband didn't finish his dinner because he didn't feel very well and now he says he has a severe pain in his chest and that he cannot breath. He looks pale and clammy.

- Mr Foxtrot telephones. His speech is slurred. He tells you that he is having a nervous breakdown and that he wants the doctor to come and see him as soon as possible.

- Mrs Armstrong telephones to say that her 14-year-old son has been complaining of abdominal pain all day. She thought he just had a 'tummy upset' at first but he now seems quite distressed and 'It just isn't like him'.

- Mrs Walsh telephones. She tells you that Adam, her 8-year-old son, is having a nose bleed. He often gets them but this one is heavier than he has had before and it has been bleeding for nearly an hour now.

- Mrs Ryan, aged 80 years, says she cannot rouse her husband.

- Mrs Baker arrives at the reception desk just after morning surgery has begun. She is carrying William, her 3-year-old son. She tells you that she has been up all night with him. He has cried all night and has been very hot. She wants to see the doctor. She does not have an appointment.

In this chapter you have learnt:

■ The most likely sources of emergency calls.

■ How to deal with different types of distressed caller.

■ The different options for responding to emergency calls.

■ How to build up your skills in dealing with emergency calls.

■ How your own practice might deal with a range of typical emergency calls.

APPENDIX 12a
Urgent call checklist

- Telephone number.
- Name.
- Address.
- Age.
- Problem.
  - How long have they had it?
  - Has this ever happened before?
  - Does the patient suffer from any major illnesses?
- Pain:
  - Where?
  - How bad?
- Bleeding:
  - Where from?
  - How much?
  - Still bleeding?
- Head injury:
  - Unconsciousness?

Vaccination and Immunisation

Vaccinations account for a significant part of a practice's workload. The Government have introduced incentives called Target Payments to encourage GPs to vaccinate more young children. The receptionist plays a vital role in maximising the number of vaccinations the practice carries out.

In this chapter you will learn:

1) The four main groups of vaccination or immunisation.

2) For each group of vaccinations you will learn:

   – why the vaccinations are important for the patient and for the practice,

   – how vaccinations are usually handled in a typical practice, and

   – the part the receptionist can play in promoting vaccinations.

3) What sources of information about vaccination and immunisation are available.

4) How to deal with the common problems that arise with vaccinations and immunisations.

INTRODUCTION
What are vaccinations?

Vaccinations are medical procedures (usually injections) that activate the body's own defence mechanisms against the effects of some transmitted diseases.

A typical example of a disease that can be prevented by vaccination is measles. Children are particularly likely to catch measles and pass it on to other children, but if a child is vaccinated at an early age this risk can be significantly reduced.

The important thing is to make sure that as many children as possible are vaccinated against common childhood illnesses, which is why in 1990 the Government introduced an incentive scheme called 'target payments'.

You need to have a fairly clear idea of what target payments are about so that you can play your part helping the practice to achieve its vaccination 'targets'.

The main types of vaccination

In this chapter vaccinations and immunisations are divided into four groups:

1) Vaccinations and immunisations which come under the target payments system.

2) Vaccinations for people travelling abroad.

3) Other routine vaccinations.

4) Influenza vaccinations.

The four groups of vaccination are now dealt with in detail.

'TARGET PAYMENT' VACCINATIONS

For convenience, this section is divided into two parts:

– a basic introduction to the concept of target payments, and

– further details about target payments.

Target payments – introduction

The target payments scheme was devised to encourage GPs to achieve a high level of immunisation for children on their lists.

Vaccinations under the target payment scheme are those given to children up to the age of 6 years. The scheme covers vaccinations against the following infections:

- Diphtheria.
- Tetanus.
- Poliomyelitis.
- Pertussis.
- Haemophilus influenza b (Hib).
- Measles, mumps, rubella (MMR).

The Department of Health wants to make sure that 90% of all children are immunised against the above diseases. This high level of vaccination reduces the incidence of the serious and possibly fatal infections that young children can catch. Some children may not be immunised because their parents refuse to have them immunised or, less commonly, because the child has some illness or condition which prevents immunisation. However, even children who have not been immunised have a measure of protection because they are less likely to catch an infection from other children who have already been immunised.

A parent's or guardian's consent is required before a child can be immunised. Each FHSA has its own form which practices use for this.

The target payments system works in the following way.

Unlike other items of service, the GP does not receive a payment for each immunisation carried out. The GP receives **no payment at all** until at least the set target number of the eligible children in the practice have been fully immunised. **Only when the target number has been reached** does the GP receive a payment from the Family Health Services Authority (FHSA). The size of the target group is based on the practice list as a whole rather than for each partner separately.

There are currently two target levels. A **higher level** (90% of the target group) and a **lower level** (70% of the target group). So if a GP immunises 90% of the eligible children on their list then they receive a **higher target payment**. If they manage a lower level of only 70% they receive a **lower target payment**. This is one-third of the higher target payment. If, however, a GP does not achieve the 70% level, they receive no payment at all – even for work done.

Vaccinations for some of the children on a GP's list may also be carried out in local health authority or school clinics. These vaccinations help the practice to achieve its target. However, if the practice earns a target payment, it is only paid for the vaccinations carried out by the practice.

You can see from the above that your doctors will probably be keen to immunise as many children as possible and your practice will need to have:

- Very accurate records of the children on their list who are in the correct age group.
- A good system for making sure that as many children as possible are immunised.
- A good system for recording work carried out and for claiming and tracking payments from the FSHA.

Your role as a receptionist

Accurately record patients' dates of birth (for example, when registering new patients).

Make sure you are clear about what, if any, immunisation sessions are held in the practice so that patients can easily be referred to them. You also need to know what 'flexible arrangements' are made by the practice to immunise children as the opportunity arises.

Be aware that, when a child is being immunised against poliomyelitis, the parents or guardians, or anyone involved in the care of that child should be encouraged to have a booster injection against poliomyelitis. The reason for this is that a child vaccinated against polio will continue to excrete live vaccine virus for several weeks and this may infect people caring for that child.

Make sure that parents' queries about immunisations are dealt with correctly by referring them to the right clinical staff.

- Find out if there are special childhood immunisation sessions in your practice or health centre. In some cases these may be included in 'mother and baby' clinics.
- Find out who normally carries out the immunisation in your practice. Is it the practice nurse or the doctors?

Target payments – further details

Now that you have learnt the basics about target payments, you need to have a slightly more detailed appreciation of how target payments are calculated.

The target payment immunisations apply to two groups of children:

- Children aged 2 years and under.
- Children aged 5 years and under – pre-school boosters.

The practice can get a target payment for each group. To count towards a target payment for a group a child must have received a *full course* of immunisation. This can involve more than one dose of a vaccine.

For **children aged 2 years and under** there are four immunisations:

1) Diphtheria/tetanus/poliomyelitis, which requires *3 doses*.
2) Pertussis (whooping cough), which requires *3 doses*.
3) Hib (haemophilus influenza b), which requires *3 doses*.
4) Mumps/measles/rubella, which requires *1 dose*.

For **children aged 5 years and under** a 'booster' dose is required, and to count towards the quarterly target payment each child has to receive a dose of the following vaccines:

1) Tetanus
2) Diphtheria. } *1 booster dose* given in one combined ampoule.
3) Polio, which requires *1 booster dose*. The polio booster comes in the form of 'drops' which are given by mouth.

Target payments are calculated and paid on a quarterly basis. The quarters for general practice begin on 1 January, 1 April, 1 July and 1 October.

Because there is a need to make sure that every child is accounted for and that all the required immunisations are carried out in each quarter a great deal of effort is made in each practice to organise target payment immunisations.

Your role as a receptionist

Co-operate with management efforts in your practice. For example, most practices will plan each quarter's immunisations well in advance.

Understand and co-operate with any opportunities the practice may take to get children immunised.

Be aware of how immunisations are dealt with in the practice and how your local Health Authority may also help with notifications, etc. For example, most Health Authorities send out reminder cards to parents when immunisations are due. The FHSA also lists children who are due to join the target group in the following quarter. This can be very useful in helping the practice to plan ahead.

Practices which are computerised very often have reminders built into the computer system. So, for example, when a child's record appears on the screen a message will 'flash' indicating that they are due for a particular immunisation.

Make sure that immunisations are correctly recorded. The following forms are used where the vaccination has been unscheduled.

■ For children under 2 years of age: form **PT\TC1** (in Scotland, GP/TC1; in Northern Ireland, TC1).

■ For children aged 5 years and under: form **FP\TPB** (in Scotland, GP/TCB; in Northern Ireland, TCB).

Encourage parents to bring their children for immunisation, but do not pressurise them.

Know how to deal with queries. Parents can often be anxious about the side-effects of immunisation or worried that their child is too ill to be immunised. You should avoid getting involved in a clinical discussion on this. Instead you should try to get the parent to speak to a nurse or doctor in the practice.

There are certain conditions where it would not be wise for the child to be immunised. This is mainly if the child is unwell with an acute infection. In this case the parent is usually advised to contact the practice in about 2 week's time.

1) Find out who in your practice is responsible for managing the whole process of childhood immunisations and what kind of help they may need from you.

2) Find out what arrangements there are for reminding parents about immunisation.

3) Find out about the systems in place for monitoring vaccination progress.

4) Find out how the practice finds out if a named child is overdue for vaccinations and how it follows up children who do not attend for immunisations.

5) Find out who you can refer parents' questions about immunisation to.

VACCINATIONS FOR PEOPLE TRAVELLING ABROAD

Patients going abroad are often exposed to infections which are not common in the UK. They can be vaccinated against the diseases listed below:

- Typhoid.*
- Paratyphoid.
- Cholera.*
- Polio.*
- Hepatitis A.*
- Yellow fever.

(*Note:* This list is current at 31 October 1995 and is subject to change according to Government policy. Your surgery should have the latest details.)

Vaccinations against diseases marked with an asterisk (*) are provided free by the NHS *provided that they are recommended for the country to be visited.* For example, polio vaccinations are not given free of charge for patients visiting Turkey.

For each vaccination the GP receives a fixed fee from the FHSA. Form FP-73 (in Scotland, GP-73; in Northern Ireland, VAC) is used to claim this fee. The GP should also list on the FP-73 the names of the countries to be visited.

Some practices carry their own supplies of vaccine, which means the patient does not have to pay for a prescription or visit the chemist. The practice can reclaim both the cost of the vaccine and a dispensing fee from the Prescription Pricing Authority.

The NHS will only pay for a vaccination from the above list if it is actually recommended for the country or area to be visited. Any other vaccinations are not covered under the NHS and the patient has to pay for them privately. Practices will either issue patients with a private prescription so that they can obtain the vaccine at a pharmacy or they may carry their own stock of some of the vaccines. Most of the rarer vaccinations are not carried out by GPs but by specialist hospitals. However, some general practices may be designated yellow fever centres.

Protection against malaria is available on private prescription. This is not a vaccination but a **chemoprophylaxis** (preventive drug therapy). The patient has to take tablets both before, during and after their stay abroad. We mention this here because, although anti-malarial treatment is not strictly a vaccination, it is relevant to the patient's vaccination needs when travelling abroad.

Find out if your practice is a yellow fever centre and, if not, where the nearest centre is.

There are also some vaccinations not on the above list which are needed for travel to remote parts of the world. Most practices will have a schedule, which they get from magazines such as *Pulse*, showing which vaccinations are recommended for different parts of the world. If you cannot locate this, the *MIMS* has a page of guidance which you can locate by looking for 'Travel vaccinations' in the 'Tables' section of the Contents.

Some vaccines may have to be given at specific times before leaving the UK. Your practice may have some basic advice about the timing of vaccinations for you to refer to when answering patients' questions. You will have patients ranging from the disorganised holiday maker to the business man who will not present for vaccination within these recommended periods. You should obtain full details on the countries to be visited and the duration of the visit and seek advice on whether the vaccine should be offered.

Vaccines may cause an allergic reaction at the injection site, with some inflammation, itching and swelling. This typically lasts about 48 hours. The injection sites themselves can also become infected. In addition, patients may complain of flu-like symptoms such as generalised muscle ache, fatigue and general malaise.

Most reactions to vaccinations are minor. Most patients put up with them, perhaps taking paracetamol to relieve any minor discomfort. If a patient is sufficiently concerned that they contact the practice for advice, it might be prudent to make an appointment for them to see the nurse or one of the doctors. Most patients will simply need reassurance, but some will require more active assistance.

Some countries require certificates of vaccination which have to be signed by the doctor. The practice is entitled to charge the patient for this certificate, which often simply takes the form of a handwritten letter.

Your role as a receptionist

You should advise patients correctly on what facilities the practice can offer for travellers' vaccinations, e.g. clinic sessions.

You will need to give general advice (if requested by your practice) about precautions and side-effects relating to vaccinations or to refer the patient to the relevant person (e.g. the practice nurse or a doctor).

You should advise patients about likely charges (if any) for vaccinations.

Know where to get specialist advice regarding the vaccine requirements for some countries.

Make sure that vaccinations are correctly recorded using form FP-73 and that the patients' records are updated. You may also need to make sure that form FP-10 (prescription form) is completed for vaccines dispensed by the practice.

1) Find out what arrangements your practice has for travellers' vaccinations. For example, is there a special clinic session for travellers?

2) Find out if your practice has any general guidance for you to use, or leaflets to give out when talking to patients about:

   ■ Travel vaccinations required.

   ■ Which order travel vaccinations are given in.

   ■ The correct intervals between doses.

   ■ What precautions to take.

   ■ What common complaints or side-effects, if any, there may be with some of the travel vaccinations.

3) Find out where your practice keeps a copy of the vaccination advice provided by drug companies or *Pulse* magazine (usually on a notice-board).

4) Find out the sources of specialist advice for travellers' vaccinations (usually the nearest hospital specialising in tropical or infectious diseases).

5) Find out what charges are made where vaccinations are given privately and for providing vaccination certificates (where required).

6) Find out which vaccines your practice stocks.

OTHER ROUTINE VACCINATIONS

This section covers all the vaccinations not covered by target payments and vaccinations for patients not travelling abroad.

The most common routine vaccines are:

- Tetanus
- Polio.
- Rubella.

A full schedule of routine vaccinations is given in Appendix 13a at the end of this chapter. Some vaccinations require more than one dose and the GP receives a fee for each dose given, except for infectious hepatitis vaccines.

In many practices the vaccinations are performed by the practice nurse who will be acting under the direction of the doctor.

Many practices will have ways of making sure that patients receive the vaccinations they require, either by raising the topic if the patient attends for a new patient examination or at a well-person or mother–and–baby clinic.

Your role as a receptionist

Be aware of what facilities the practice has for vaccinations, e.g. special clinics.

Co-operate with practice initiatives to opportunely vaccinate the appropriate patients. For example:

■ Parents of new-born children may be encouraged to have a booster injection against poliomyelitis. Even grandparents may be included in this category.

■ The practice may have a policy of actively encouraging tetanus vaccinations in line with current NHS guidelines and clinical need.

Refer patients' queries to the correct member of staff.

Make sure that vaccinations are correctly recorded using form FP-73, and that they are recorded in the patient's medical records.

Where the practice supplies its own vaccine, make sure that a FP-10 form is filled in and given to the appropriate person in the practice.

1) Find out what arrangements there are in your practice for vaccinating adults, e.g. special clinic sessions and practice nurse sessions.

2) Locate the *Immunisation against Infectious Disease* book and look up the paragraphs which cover the various categories of 'at risk' patients who require vaccinations.

INFLUENZA VACCINATIONS

Influenza is usually a self-limiting illness, but it can be serious for some people. Influenza vaccinations are usually given during the autumn and are only given to patients whose health is such they might be badly affected by catching influenza. Typical examples of such patients are:

■ Elderly patients.

■ Patients with lung disease.

■ Patients with heart disease.

■ Diabetic patients.

- Patients with kidney disease.
- Patients who are suffering from a general debility.
- Any patient whose ability to cope with infection is compromised in some way.

You may find that many patients who aren't in the above categories ask for an influenza vaccination. For the 'worried well' (low-risk patients who are well but are worried about catching an infection) most practices will give a vaccination if they have sufficient stocks of the vaccine. Your practice may have a policy about this. Some practices make special arrangements for influenza vaccinations in October and November.

Most practices purchase stocks of the vaccine and are reimbursed by the NHS[1] for every unit dispensed. To do this an FP-10 form is filled in for every patient receiving the vaccine. Where the vaccine is not stocked in the practice the patient is given a prescription instead.

Influenza vaccines don't prevent respiratory infection occurring from some source other than the specific strain vaccinated against. This may cause some patients to complain that the treatment hasn't worked.

Your role as a receptionist

Make sure that patients requesting the influenza vaccination are given correct information about the availability of the vaccine and clinic sessions.

Apply the practice policy for informing patients if they are eligible for the vaccination.

Refer queries to the correct person in the practice.

If the practice has bought stocks of the influenza vaccine, participate in the stock control systems set up by the practice manager. (*Note:* not all practices buy in their own stocks of influenza vaccine. Many practices simply give the patients' prescriptions to take to the pharmacist.)

1) Find out if your practice has special arrangements for influenza vaccinations in the autumn or early winter.

2) Ask if your practice has a procedure for checking whether patients can receive the influenza vaccinations.

[1] This policy is correct at the time of publication but may change.

3) Find out if the practice has any guidance about influenza vaccinations that you are allowed to use when dealing with patients' enquiries.

In this chapter you learnt about:

- Target payments.
- Vaccinations for patients travelling abroad.
- Routine vaccinations.
- Influenza vaccinations.
- The role of the receptionist in assisting the practice with the above groups of vaccinations:
  - accurate record keeping,
  - knowing where to find sources of information, and
  - dealing with patients' or parents' enquiries.

APPENDIX 13a
List of vaccinations

Many of the vaccinations listed below are only given to patients who are 'at risk' in some way because of their profession.

The NHS will pay for the vaccinations listed below *provided that the patient falls into the correct category*. For example, rubella vaccinations can only be paid for by the FHSA if given to women.

Vaccine	Groups of people for whom the FHSA will pay a vaccination fee
Tetanus (*NB:* Not payable for travelling, when given as a routine measure)	If not previously immunised – children 15–19 years of age *or* on leaving school; persons after leaving school. If previously immunised – persons on leaving school or entering higher education or starting work; thereafter persons who have not had a reinforcing dose in: 1) the previous 5 years, and then 2) the previous 5–15 years.
Poliomyelitis	Persons over 6 years old and under 40 years old and: 1) *parents or guardians of children being given oral polio vaccine,* 2) special risk groups such as GPs and general practice staff who come into contact with patients, 3) ambulance staff, 4) medical students, 5) practising dentists, 6) nursing and other hospital staff who come into contact with patients, 7) certain public health staff, 8) the families of the above groups, 9) laboratory staff likely to handle material contaminated with the polio virus.

	If previously immunised but without receiving a reinforcing dose:
	1) persons aged 6 years and over at school, or on leaving school, or on entering higher education, or starting work.
MMR	Children aged 6–15 years who have not previously been immunised with MMR combined vaccine
Measles (single antigen)	Children aged 6–15 years who have not been immunised against measles, and who have not had measles
Rubella	1) Girls between their 10th and 14th birthdays who have not previously been immunised with MMR combined vaccine
	2) Women of child-bearing age who are not pregnant and who are not immune to rubella
	3) Male staff working in ante-natal clinics who are seronegative.
Typhoid Paratyphoid	Staff in hospitals considered to be at risk of infection
Infectious Hepatitis (Hep A)	Persons in institutions who are exposed to a high risk of infection and for whom vaccination is recommended by the Medical Officer of the Environmental Health Department
Diphtheria	Only required if traveller going to an area where there is a risk
Rabies	Groups at special risk such as staff working in:
	1) kennels and catteries used for quarantine,
	2) quarantine premises in zoos,
	3) laboratories handling the rabies virus,

4) seaports or airports where
    contact with imported animals is likely,

5) companies transporting imported dogs, cats,
    etc.

Anthrax

Only for workers in tanneries, glue, gelatine,
soap and bone meal factories, and those in
woollen mills regularly handling imported raw
materials such as goat hair and wool

NOTE: The list above is current at 31 October 1995. However, changes in
NHS policy may cause the list to be altered. The Department of Health regu-
larly distributes to all practices a guide entitled *Immunisation against Infectious
Diseases,* which should be available for you to consult.

Contraception and Cervical Cytology

Both contraception and cervical cytology are important services for the promotion of health.

As well as providing considerable health benefits for patients, the practice itself gains income from the various fees involved.

As a receptionist you will find that you have an important role to play in making sure the patients can obtain these services easily.

In this chapter you will learn:

1) The different methods of contraception that are available on the NHS.

2) Other sources of contraception or contraceptive advice.

3) Abortion.

4) How GPs are paid for contraceptive services and what forms and documentation are required.

5) What cervical cytology is and why it is provided.

6) The importance of the cervical cytology recall systems.

7) The target payments system for cervical cytology.

Before you start – you will find it useful to locate copies of the following forms: FP-1001, FP-1003 and FP-1002 (if your doctors fit IUCDs – otherwise known as the 'coil').

CONTRACEPTION

Contraceptive advice is a useful service provided by general practitioners. It provides GPs with an opportunity to meet healthy patients who might otherwise infrequently see a GP. The patient's request for contraceptive advice gives the GP an opportunity to acquire information for health promotion targets, check the patient's cervical cytology status and give advice about any issue raised. Providing contraceptive advice also generates an item of service payment for the practice.

The contraceptive list

Patients receiving contraceptive services from the practice should join the practice's Contraceptive List using form **FP-1001** (In Scotland, GP-102; in Northern Ireland, GP-1001).

The Contraceptive List is distinct from the practice's General Medical Services (GMS) List. A patient on the Contraceptive List does not have to be on the doctor's GMS list. Generally, most if not all patients on the Contraceptive List will also be on the GMS list.

See also
Chapter 8
on FHSA
forms

The patient should sign an FP-1001 when they receive contraceptive advice – they do not have to actually be prescribed a drug or appliance. If the patient is not asked to sign form FP-1001 then the practice's income will be reduced. If there is a delay in asking the patient to sign the form or in sending it to the Family Health Services Authority (FHSA) the practice income flow will be slowed.

The receptionist's role in contraceptive services

- You should know what contraceptive services are available in the practice and which doctors and nurses provide them.
- You should know how to help patients to use the practice's contraception services.
- Having helped the patient you should then think about the practice. You should be able to use the practice's manual or computer system quickly to check if the patient is on the Contraceptive List.
- You should know when you should ask a patient to complete an FP-1001.

Methods of contraception

Combined pill

This is the most popular form of oral contraception because it is easy to use and is very effective. The combined pill contains two different hormones. However, the combined pill is not without risk and the doctor will not offer it to certain women in at-risk groups.

For most brands of combined pill, the woman takes tablets for 21 days and then has 7 pill-free days.

The doctor will want to check the patient's blood pressure regularly, say every 6 months.

Progesterone only pill

This is also known as the **mini-pill**. The woman takes a tablet every day at the same time. There are no pill-free days. The mini-pill is less effective than the combined pill. Patients for whom the combined pill is unsuitable may be able to take the mini-pill.

Depo-Provera

This is a slow-release drug given every 12–13 weeks by injection. The drug leaches from its oily suspension and maintains contraceptive protection over the 12–13 weeks.

Intrauterine contraceptive device (IUCD or coil)

The IUCD is a mechanical device inserted into the womb. It is most suitable for the older woman who has already had some children. The IUCD is replaced every 5 years.

If a patient has had an IUCD fitted in the practice, she should sign form FP-1002 (in Scotland, GP-103; in Northern Ireland, FP-1002).

Cap (diaphragm)

Caps or diaphragms are inserted into the vagina to cover the cervix. They come in different sizes to suit different women. The patient must be taught how to use a diaphragm by a doctor or nurse.

Norplant

This contraceptive drug is contained in six small rods that are inserted just beneath the skin in the arm. Norplant offers effective contraception for 5 years. It is a minor surgical procedure to insert and remove this drug. Similar methods of delivering contraceptive drugs using only one rod are in development.

Vasectomy and tubal ligation

More permanent forms of contraception are vasectomy for the male and tubal ligation for the female.

Women requesting tubal ligation (sometimes referred to as *'having their tubes tied'*) require referral to a specialist.

A few practices provide vasectomy as an in-house procedure but most have to refer the patient to a specialist. When a couple who seek contraceptive advice decide that the man should be referred for a vasectomy, the woman should sign form FP-1001.

The 'morning-after' pill (MAP)

This is a form of post-coital contraception, i.e. a contraceptive method that can be used *after* intercourse. From time to time, you will receive a call from an anxious woman requesting the morning-after pill. She will usually have had a contraceptive accident or omitted to take appropriate contraceptive precautions. Less commonly, she might be a victim of a sexual assault. You must find out what the practice's response to such patients is so that you can answer her enquiry promptly.

Some doctors do not prescribe the morning-after pill because of their personal or religious beliefs. The pill can be given up to 72 hours after unprotected intercourse. The pill (see Schering PC4 in *MIMS*) can cause nausea and vomiting. You can appreciate that the drug does not work very well if the patient vomits it back up. To get around this side-effect, the doctor will generally also prescribe an anti-emetic drug (a drug to counteract vomiting) such as Motilium or Maxolon.

The IUCD can also be used as a form of post-coital contraception.

Condoms

GPs cannot prescribe condoms, but they may advise patients to use them. The Family Planning Association does issue condoms to its clients. Sometimes, GPs can supply condoms as part of a local initiative to combat the spread of HIV.

Combinations of methods

To increase the level of contraceptive protection, couples may combine different methods. For example, a couple might use both the cap and condoms.

- Ask your manager what contraceptive services are available in the practice.
- What is the practice's policy on the morning-after pill?
- Find out how you are to handle a patient who rings up asking for the morning-after pill.

How does the patient obtain contraceptive services provided by the practice?

Patients wishing to receive contraceptive advice generally make a routine appointment to see the doctor. Following the consultation, the doctor should get the patient to sign form FP-1001 in the consulting room, or ask the patient to call at the reception desk and sign it there.

Some patients will have to come to special surgery sessions such as *well-woman clinics* or *family planning clinics* if they are going to use devices such as the IUCD or the cap. The minor surgery session might be appropriate for patients wishing to have Norplant.

The practice nurses may play a role in the provision of contraceptive services. They might simply check lifestyle habits, weight and blood pressure or, if they have suitable training in contraception, may provide patients with advice on contraception. Practice nurses often have more time to discuss issues with patients.

Many practices do not provide all of the available contraceptive methods. Some do not fit IUCDs, either because the doctors have not had the necessary training or because the practice cannot allocate the required time.

Some doctors do not provide contraceptive services at all because of their own moral or religious beliefs. Other doctors will not recommend the IUCD or the morning-after pill, again because of their personal beliefs.

A practice offering contraceptive services is not restricted to providing the facility only to its own patients. Patients from other practices are allowed to join your Contraceptive List. This situation could arise if the patient's own GP does not provide contraceptive services, or if a woman does not want to use her own GP's contraceptive services, perhaps because the GP is a friend or simply because she wants a female doctor to provide her with contraceptive advice.

Some patients using the practice's contraceptive services may be quite young. You must always respect their privacy. They will hopefully have received sufficient professional counselling about the issues of contraception and sexual relationships. You should never say anything that might appear critical or disapproving to these young patients. To do so would compromise patient care and put you at risk of disciplinary procedures.

Ask your manager if there are any doctors in the practice who do not wish to be involved in any aspects of contraceptive services or terminations of pregnancy.

If so, find out how the practice deals with the issue.

The Family Planning Association

The Family Planning Association is another provider of contraceptive services. The Association has clinics in most areas and will often supply forms of contraception not provided by GPs. The Association also does cervical smears and often provides more general 'well-woman' services.

- Find out the address and telephone number of the local Family Planning Association clinics.
- Ask your practice manager when you should refer a patient to the Family Planning Association clinic.

Contraceptive services for temporary resident patients

A temporary resident patient may approach the practice seeking contraceptive services. Often these will be patients already using some form of contraception. You should manage these patients in the same way as your normal patients. However, form FP-1003 (in Scotland, GP-104; in Northern Ireland, 1003) is used instead of the FP-1001. If contraceptive advice is the only service provided to the patient, then only form FP-1003 is required. If, however, the patient receives general medical services either on the same occasion or later, you should ask them to complete form FP-19 as well.

Form FP-1001

This is a four-part form; Part Four is on the back of Part Two. When the FP-1001 is completed, Part One is given to the patient, Part Two is sent to the FHSA, and Part Three is kept by the practice.

Form FP-1001 expires after 12 months and the patient must sign a new form each year if they continue to receive contraceptive services from the practice. The patient can sign the new FP-1001 between 1 month before the expiry of the previous form and 6 months after the date of expiry. For example, if a woman signs an FP-1001 on 3 April 1994 and continues to receive contraceptive services, a further FP-1001 can be signed sometime between 3 March 1995 and 3 October 1995. Wherever possible you should get new FP-1001 forms signed as soon as possible in order to avoid missing payment claims and to assist cash flow.

The date on which future FP-1001 forms are due is the anniversary of the first FP-1001 and not the date on which the last FP-1001 was signed. For example, if a woman signs her first FP-1001 on 5 June 1993 and signs a new FP-1001 on 8 August 1994, then her next FP-1001 is due to be signed (provided that she continues to receive contraceptive services from the practice) on 5 June 1995 and not 8 August 1995.

When you are completing a *renewal* FP-1001 there are two further statements on the back of the form (Part Four) that must also be completed:

■ You should enter the date of the previous FP-1001 in the space provided and tick the adjacent box.

■ If the FP-1001 is being completed more than 1 year after the previous form, then you must apply for the payment to be continuous by ticking the second box on the back of the form. If you fail to tick this box then the practice can lose up to two quarters' (6 months) FP-1001 payment.

> How would you find out if the patient needs to sign a new FP-1001? Find out what systems, manual or computerised, are in the practice to tell you when a new form is needed.

The GP must sign and date the form. You should make sure that you stamp the practice's name and address in the appropriate space in Part Four. When the FP-1001 is completed you may have to record details of the form in a manual or computerised practice system. There should be a minimum delay between the completion of the FP-1001 and its dispatch to the FHSA.

1) Find out where forms FP-1003 and FP-1002 are kept, study them both and ask your manager how you should complete them.

2) Find out how you should help a patient obtain the various types of contraception available in the practice. For example, patients requiring the pill would probably be seen in routine surgery, whereas patients wanting a cap or IUCD would probably be seen in a special clinic.

3) Find out what you should do with a patient who telephones saying she has no contraceptive pills left and needs to start a new packet that night.

THERAPEUTIC ABORTION

The Abortion Act (1967) provides for therapeutic abortion under certain conditions. Two doctors must declare in writing that the proposal to terminate the pregnancy satisfies the requirements of the Act. The patient is always referred to a specialist centre. Therapeutic abortions (terminations of pregnancy (TOP)) are available under the NHS. In addition, the British Pregnancy Advisory Service (BPAS) provides a private (non-NHS) service.

Some doctors will not take any part in therapeutic abortions because of their personal beliefs. Others will refer the patient to an appropriate specialist, but will not sign the documentation.

Receptionists may also have beliefs that make it difficult for them to participate in therapeutic abortions. The receptionist's involvement in a therapeutic abortion could involve tasks such as typing the referral letter, liaising with hospital departments and the patient about appointment times, and filing correspondence. If you would find this distressing, then you should discuss the issue with your manager.

No matter what personal beliefs you have, you should never say or intimate anything judgemental to the patient or criticise her actions in any way. To do so could compromise patient care and thus put you at risk of disciplinary action.

Most patients recover quickly after a therapeutic abortion, but there are some who will develop complications such as abnormal bleeding or infection. Some of these patients may be quite ill and require the practice's priority assistance.

1) How do you feel about therapeutic abortions? Do they present you with a serious moral dilemma? Discuss your feelings about this with the practice manager.

2) What role does your practice expect of you in managing therapeutic abortions?

3) How will you handle the patient who becomes ill after a therapeutic abortion?

4) Find the telephone number of the BPAS.

CERVICAL CYTOLOGY

Before you start this part of the chapter – find a cervical smear test form. At least make sure you know what such forms look like and where they are kept. Ask your manager if you are expected to fill any part of it in.

A cervical smear is a screening test for detecting changes in the cells in the neck of the womb (the cervix). These changes may suggest that the patient is at risk of developing cancer of the cervix. Sometimes the smear will show that the patient has already developed cancer of the cervix.

The receptionist's role in cervical cytology

■ Know about the clinical importance of regular cervical smears for the patient.

■ Know about the financial importance of cervical cytology for the practice.

- Understand the call and recall systems used by your practice and by other authorities such as the FHSA.

- Know how the practice provides cervical smears for its patients.

- Know how to use the practice's manual or computerised systems to find out if a patient is due for her cervical smear.

- Know what the practice expects you to do if a patient is due for a cervical smear.

- Know how to process smear results. In particular, know how to identify an abnormal result.

Clinical and financial importance of cervical cytology

Cervical smears are a worthwhile activity for the practice for both clinical and financial reasons.

From a clinical point of view, detecting the changes in the cervix that precede the actual cancer is well worthwhile, as early changes are normally completely treatable. If a patient develops actual cancer of the cervix, the situation becomes more fraught. If the disease is detected early, surgery may be curative. Detected late, cancer of the cervix is often fatal. Two thousand women in the UK die each year from cervical cancer.

Financially, cervical cytology earns money for the practice. The doctors will receive payments from the FHSA if a certain percentage of the practice's female patients have had cervical smears.

Call and recall programmes

Patients are called and recalled for cervical smears by means of cytology screening programmes. These programmes are generally well organised. Screening programmes are run by both GPs and the FHSA.

Your local hospital may maintain a register of patients who have had previous abnormal smears. They may write to the practice asking what has happened to a patient if no repeat smear is received when recommended.

Screening programmes target women aged between 20 and 65 years. Doctors also encourage women aged under 20 years who are sexually active to have cervical smears.

Many doctors would advise patients to have a smear test every 3 years. A patient who has just had her first smear will often be advised to have a second smear within a shorter period, say 1 year, to counter the risk of a false-negative result. A false-negative result is where a test is reported as *normal* when in fact the result is *abnormal*.

Patients who have had a previously abnormal smear will usually be recalled more frequently, often annually.

Your practice may have a system to prompt you if a patient is overdue for a smear test. This may consist of a simple piece of card in the patient's notes or a message on a computer screen when you access the patient's computerised records.

1) Ask your manager how the practice's patients get called and recalled for their cervical smears.

■ Does the practice have its own recall system for cervical cytology?

■ Who runs it?

■ Are you expected to play any role in it?

2) Ask your practice manager to show you how you would find out if a patient is overdue for a cervical smear. Find out what you should do if you notice that a patient is overdue for smear.

3) Ask your practice manager how you should deal with a woman who is anxious about having a cervical smear.

Hysterectomies and cervical smears

Women who have had a *total hysterectomy* do not need to have cervical smears. A total hysterectomy is where the entire uterus (womb), i.e. including the cervix, is removed. The final decision on whether a patient should be included in the cervical cytology recall system should always rest with a doctor or nurse. However, you will find it useful to have some understanding of the factors involved.

A *subtotal hysterectomy* is where only the body of the uterus is removed. The cervix is left. *These women still need cervical smears.*

There are two basic ways of doing a hysterectomy: abdominal hysterectomy and vaginal hysterectomy. A patient who has had a *vaginal hysterectomy* has had a total hysterectomy and does not need cervical smears. *Abdominal hysterectomy* could be either total or subtotal. Most hysterectomies are *total*.

You may be confused by some patients having smears despite the fact that they have had a total hysterectomy. These women are having *vault smears*, typically as a follow-up to gynaecological malignancy.

Cervical cytology targets

Cervical cytology forms the basis for a target payment scheme. The target group comprises female patients aged between 25 and 64 years inclusive (in Scotland between 20 and 60 years). Women who have had a total hysterectomy are excluded from the target group.

Women in the target group must have had a valid smear during the preceding 66 months. A valid smear is one that is not reported as *inadequate*.

The FHSA awards a lower level target payment if 50% of the target group have had a valid smear and a higher level target payment if 80% have had a valid smear. The actual amount of the payment depends on the percentage of smears done within general medical services, i.e. by a GP (or someone employed by a GP, e.g. a practice nurse or an assistant doctor).

Managing the practice's cervical cytology recall system and target achievement is very much a back room task. Most systems will include some or all of the following features:

- A record of the names of the women in the target group.
- A log of the women who have had a total hysterectomy.
- A method of letting the FHSA know which patients have had a total hysterectomy (this is important as it stops the FHSA sending recall letters to these patients and ensures that they are excluded from the target group).
- A mailing facility to tell patients when they are due for a smear test.
- A system to monitor what happens to patients whose smear test results are abnormal in some way.
- A way of calculating target achievement, preferably with an ability to look ahead to future quarters.

Processing smear results

Smear test results must be processed from both a clinical and an administrative point of view.

Clinical processing

Smear results are reported in a standard way. They are given a number from 1 to 8 and a corresponding textual description. For example, result code 2 means that the smear is normal.

A cervical smear may be reported as inadequate (result code 1). This means that the laboratory could not make a valid comment on the smear because insufficient material had been collected on the smear. A patient whose smear is reported as inadequate must have another test.

Abnormal smear results, i.e. those with a numerical result code 3–8, must be seen by a doctor. The doctor may need to take some action, ranging from advising a repeat smear within a few months to urgently referring the patient to hospital.

Laboratory technicians can detect infection in smears. In this case, the laboratory may recommend repeating the smear after the infection has been treated.

You should never file a smear report with a result code of 3 or more unless it has been seen by a doctor.

1) Look in the day's laboratory reports and find a cervical smear report. Find the following features:

The patient identifiers – name, date of birth, address.

Who did the test – important for calculating the target payment.

The test result – this is generally expressed as a number with a corresponding text explanation. The numbers signify 1, an inadequate smear; 2, a normal result; 3–8, abnormal result.

2) Find out what you should do when you find an abnormal smear result in the incoming post.

Administrative processing

Smear results must also be managed administratively to ensure that patients are recalled appropriately and that the practice's target calculation is correct.

Your manager will probably have set in place a system for monitoring cervical cytology target performance. The information required by the system will include:

■ the patient's name and date of birth.

■ The name of the person who did the smear.

■ The test result.

■ The date of next recall.

The task of actually giving test results to patients is discussed in Chapter 11.

In this chapter you learnt:

■ The main types of contraception, and which of them are obtainable on the NHS.

■ Other sources of contraceptive advice.

■ Arrangements for therapeutic abortion.

■ The different forms used for the above services.

■ Arrangements for cervical cytology:

　－ call and recall programmes, and

　－ cervical cytology target payments.

Maternity Care

Maternity care is one of the more pleasant aspects of general practice. The aim of maternity care is to ensure the well-being of both mother and baby.

In this chapter you will learn:

1) The documentation needed for maternity patients.

2) The different types of maternity care available.

3) GP services at different stages of the pregnancy.

4) Other professionals involved, e.g. midwives and health visitors.

5) Problems that may arise with pregnancy.

6) The receptionist's role in maternity services.

Before you start – you should obtain the following items:

- an obstetric calculator,
- a form FP-24,
- a form FW-8, and
- a form Mat-B1.

INTRODUCTION

Because pregnant women are usually quite well, maternity care is really *maternity surveillance* – checking the pregnant woman at regular intervals to ensure that she continues to be well and that her pregnancy is progressing satisfactorily.

Maternity care offers the GP an opportunity to get to know the pregnant woman better. This should enhance the professional relationship and may help the GP to anticipate problems, or to identify problems at an early stage.

Many difficulties experienced during pregnancy are minor, but sometimes more serious problems occur. Early diagnosis of problems allows early intervention or planned management and avoids crisis management at a later point.

We start by discussing your role in maternity care, including the use of the obstetric calculator, and then move on to cover the three main stages of pregnancy:

— ante-natal care,
— the delivery, and
— post-natal care.

THE RECEPTIONIST'S ROLE IN MATERNITY CARE

When a patient tells you that she is pregnant, you should listen carefully to what she is telling you in case she is not pleased to be in that state. You should watch her body language to help you pick up indications of her feelings.

If it is not at all clear that the woman is happy to be pregnant, you should simply offer to arrange an appointment for her to see the doctor.

If it is clear that the woman is happy to be pregnant, you should:

- Ensure that she signs form **FP-24** (in Scotland, GP-24; in Northern Ireland, MMS1). A discussion on completing form FP-24 is in the Appendix 15a at the end of this chapter.
- Make an appointment for her to come to the practice's ante-natal clinic.
- Ask her if she has been given a form **FW-8** exempting her from prescription charges. If not, you should ask one of the doctors or the midwives to sign one for her.
- Your practice might have prepared information packs for newly pregnant women. If this is the case, you should give one to her.

When you are on duty at the reception desk during the ante-natal clinic, you should make sure that there is a valid FP-24 for each woman attending.

You need to be aware of the urgent or emergency situations that can arise in pregnancy. Bleeding, loss of fetal movement and very early onset of labour pains are symptoms that you should report promptly to the duty doctor. At the end of this chapter there are some scenarios of emergencies for you to consider and discuss with your practice manager.

Many of your pregnant women will require a **Mat–B1** form. They give this form to their employers for Statutory Maternity Pay (SMP) purposes. It should be given after 26 weeks gestation. An obstetric calculator (see below) will prove useful in quickly telling you if the Mat-B1 can be issued. The Mat B1 may be signed by either a doctor or a midwife. No fee is payable.

Calculating the gestation

Gestation is a measure of how advanced a pregnancy is. Gestation is expressed in weeks. Pregnant women will often measure their gestation in months. When taking details of any problem or request, you should establish the gestation in weeks.

When a woman gives birth, she is said to have *been confined* or to *have delivered*. The *estimated date of confinement or delivery* (EDC or EDD) is the date on which the woman is expected to have her baby.

The gestation and the estimated date of confinement are calculated from the date of the first day of the last menstrual period (LMP). An **obstetric calculator** is a simple device, generally made of plastic, that can be used to calculate the EDC. The calculator has a calendar on the outer ring. You rotate the inner ring to line up an arrow with the woman's LMP. Another arrow now indicates the EDC. The current gestation can also be read off the obstetric calculator.

1) Ask your practice manager to demonstrate the use of the obstetric calculator.

2) Ask your practice manager to go over form FP-24 with you (see Appendix 15a at the end of this chapter). Make sure you understand what is expected of you when you

find out that a woman is pregnant. Is there a written procedure for you to follow?

ANTE-NATAL CARE

The pregnant woman will receive ante-natal care from the community midwives, the hospital ante-natal clinic and the GP – so called *shared ante-natal care*. To provide adequate communication between the various professionals, the pregnant woman generally holds her own maternity records.

The hospital obstetricians and the GPs in your area will probably have agreed a standard protocol for ante-natal care. A typical scheme for the uncomplicated maternity patient would be as follows:

- Shortly after diagnosis of pregnancy the patient visits the hospital for a *booking visit* and perhaps an ultrasound scan. Increasingly, the patient might have her *booking visit* either at the community midwife's clinic or even in her own home.
- The patient sees her GP or the community midwife:
  - every 4 weeks up to 28 weeks gestation, and
  - every two weeks up to 36 weeks gestation.
- The patient attends the hospital sometime between 30 and 36 weeks gestation.
- The patient sees her GP or the community midwife every week until *delivery*.
- The patient may be given an appointment to attend the hospital clinic at around 41 or 42 weeks gestation. This appointment is made in case the woman has not already *delivered*.

Find out how often your pregnant patients should be seen by the doctor, the midwives and the hospital ante-natal clinic.

Maternity care in general practice offers advantages to the woman. She will generally see the same faces every time she visits the practice. In addition, the GP's surgery and the community midwife's clinic are often nearer to her home than the hospital.

Maternity services are also important to the practice for financial reasons. As a guide to this, practices in England earned an average of £1.45 in 1994 from maternity services for each and every patient on their list. A practice with 8000 patients earned £11 600 that year from maternity services. You will find a table at the back of *MedEconomics* showing you the average earnings per patient for various items of services, including maternity.

A woman receiving maternity medical services from the practice does not have to be registered with the practice for her general medical needs. This complicated arrangement could arise if the woman wishes to have her baby at home when her own GP does not offer this service and your practice does.

GPs generally have maternity care clinics or ante-natal clinics separate from their routine surgeries, but some practitioners may see their maternity patients during normal surgeries as a matter of routine. Even where the doctor normally sees maternity patients in a separate *ante-natal clinic*, some patients will be seen in routine surgery. Such patients might include:

■ Women who do not want to take time off work to attend the routine ante-natal clinic.

■ Women who are well advanced in their pregnancy, say more than 32 weeks gestation, and must be seen more frequently. If their reviews at the ante-natal clinic are disrupted by, say, public holidays, then they should be seen in normal surgeries.

■ Women who have developed a problem such as elevated blood pressure who may need to be seen again before the next ante-natal clinic.

The community midwives may also run maternity care clinics in your surgery. These clinics may run at the same time as the doctor's ante-natal clinic. Midwives are increasingly providing a greater part of ante-natal care.

Pregnant women, especially those expecting their first child, are usually encouraged to attend other groups such as parentcraft classes.

For the receptionist, the ante-natal clinic is usually more relaxed than routine surgery. You get less of the stress associated with ill patients and their relatives and very little of the angst of requests for urgent appointments. The clinic should be quite a social event.

1) Find out if your doctors are on the FHSA's Obstetric List.

2) Find out what maternity care clinics are provided by the doctors and the community midwives in the surgery.

3) Do the community midwives have a clinic somewhere else in the area, such as at the local cottage hospital?

4) Ask your manager how you should help a woman to make an appointment for an ante-natal clinic.

5) Find out if your doctors support home deliveries.

6) Ask your manager how you would contact the community midwives.

Rubella and pregnancy

Rubella, also known as *German measles*, is a minor insignificant viral infection in the non-pregnant individual. However, should a non-immune pregnant woman contract rubella, the fetus will also develop the infection and will have a high risk of being born with eye problems, heart problems, deafness, mental handicap or any combination of these.

All children (male and female) are offered the MMR (measles, mumps and rubella) vaccine just after their first birthday. At present, all girls are also offered a rubella vaccination in their early teens, although this is likely to cease soon. Vaccination is effective but does not always provide life-long immunity.

Pregnant women worry about rubella infection and will contact the practice if they believe they may have been exposed to it. Before you refer the case to the doctor, you must obtain the woman's medical records. The doctor will want to know the result of any blood test the woman may have had to determine the status of her rubella immunity.

Pregnant women have their rubella immunity tested (a blood test) when they attend for their booking visit at the hospital. There may be a copy of the test report in the patient's GP records or in her shared care maternity records. If not, then you will have to telephone either the laboratory or the maternity unit to find out the patient's most recent rubella immunity report.

Miscarriage

Between 25% and 33% of all pregnancies end in miscarriage. Most miscarriages occur before 12 weeks gestation, but later miscarriages do also occur. A report of vaginal bleeding in early pregnancy can suggest that the woman is *threatening* to miscarry.

When you become aware that a patient has miscarried, you should make sure you relay the news to the doctor, the midwife and the practice manager. You may hear the news from one of the patient's relatives before the doctor receives a report from the hospital.

The practice manager will want to send the patient's FP-24 to the FHSA. Also, he or she will want to record the miscarriage on the practice's information systems and cancel hospital ante-natal appointments.

Termination of pregnancy

Some patients who have booked for maternity care will change their mind and decide instead to have the pregnancy terminated. The miscarriage fee (see Appendix 15a at the end of this chapter) is payable in this situation. The practice manager will need to manage this situation much as he or she would a miscarriage. Also, make sure you tell the doctor.

See also Chapter 14 on contraception and cervical cytology

THE ONSET OF LABOUR

You will receive telephone calls from patients who may think they are in labour. Regular contractions occurring, say, every 10 minutes or less suggest the onset of labour. Another important symptom of the onset of labour is rupture of the membranes – the patient might say that her 'waters have gone'. You need to be able to recognise these statements when an anxious or excited woman telephones the practice.

The average pregnancy lasts about 40 weeks. However, the onset of labour after 38 weeks' gestation is within normal limits. The onset of labour before 38 weeks gestation is regarded as premature labour. Obviously, the degree of prematurity is crucial – delivery at 36 weeks' gestation is not as serious as delivery at 28 weeks.

You will need to discuss the management of these telephone calls with your practice manager. Options for management include contacting one of the practice's doctors or midwives urgently, or advising the patient to go to the maternity unit at the local hospital.

POST-NATAL CARE

You will learn that a patient has *delivered* when her husband or partner, or another member of her family, brings in the hospital discharge letter. You should ask how everyone is. This is normal social practice and provides you with an opportunity to find out if there is anything you should relay to the doctor.

Post-natal visits

Your doctors will probably visit the mother during the first few days after her discharge from hospital. These visits are called *post-natal visits*. On busier days, the doctor may choose to defer these post-natal visits for a day or two unless there is a particular problem concerning the mother or the baby. Therefore, when you hear that a patient has *delivered* and is now home, you should find out whether there is anything worrying them. If there is a problem, make sure that you record a summary of it in the calls book and tell the mother's relative when the doctor will visit. If there is no obvious problem, then you could tell the relative that the doctor will visit in the next day or two.

The community's midwife also visits the woman regularly. If he or she notices a problem, they may contact the practice asking for assistance, which might be a prescription to alleviate a minor but troublesome problem or might be a request for a home visit from the doctor.

As well as addressing the clinical needs of the patient, the visiting doctor will also wish to get some forms signed:

- **FP-58/ FP-1** Form FP-58 is used to add the new baby to the practice list (in Scotland form GP-58). The Registrar of Births and Deaths will give the FP-58 to the parents when they register the child's birth. If the parents do not yet have the FP-58, then the doctor should get the parents to sign form FP-1. The FP-1 should be endorsed 'New Baby'. At least one-quarter's registration fee can be lost if form FP-1 is not completed when the FP-58 is not available.

- **FP/CHS** If the practice provides child health surveillance, form FP/CHS should be completed.

- **FP-1001** A post-natal visit is an ideal opportunity to discuss contraception.

When you know that the doctor is going to visit a patient post-natally, you should attach each of these forms to the woman's medical record. If your practice has an information pack for new mothers, attach one of these to the record.

Post-natal examination

It is common practice to offer the patient a post-natal examination. The FHSA will pay a fee if the woman has the post-natal examination between 6 and 12 weeks after her delivery.

Many practices send a post-natal appointment to the woman through the post. If the woman does not keep the appointment, the post-natal examination fee is still payable.

The post-natal examination is an ideal opportunity for the GP to remind the mother of other services provided by the practice, such as child health surveillance, routine childhood vaccinations, cervical cytology and contraceptive services. The examination also provides a suitable occasion for obtaining information for inclusion in the practice's health promotion data. You will need to get the various forms ready for completion when required.

Stillbirth

Stillbirth is the birth of a dead child after 24 weeks' gestation. It is a major tragedy for the woman and her family. If you should receive a message from the midwife or the maternity hospital that one of your patients has suffered a stillbirth, you should make sure that you effectively communicate this information to the patient's doctor and to the practice manager.

The doctor will need to be aware as soon as possible, as such a patient's needs are different. The practice manager needs to know so that routine invitations for child health surveillance and childhood vaccination sessions are not sent to the family's home.

The GP and the community midwife will visit the patient post-natally.

MATERNITY CARE FOR TEMPORARILY RESIDENT PATIENTS

A pregnant woman temporarily resident in your practice area may require maternity services from your practice. You should complete a form **FP-24** and ensure that the patient signs it. Box C on Part Two should be ticked and you should enter the name of the doctor looking after the woman in her home area.

When the woman leaves your area, you should enter the date of last service to the patient in Section (viii) on Part Three of the form and send it to the FHSA for payment.

If the woman should need general medical services as well during her stay in your area, you should ensure that form **FP-19** is also completed.

For each of the following scenarios, make some notes about what you would do and then discuss your plan with your manager:

- Sally Avon telephones you and tells you that she has just started to bleed vaginally. She is at 9 weeks' gestation.

- Tom Bister telephones to say that he has just come home to find his wife very upset. She has told him that she has not felt the baby move all day.

- Julie Coster telephones to say that she is having contractions every 15 minutes on average. She is only at 30 weeks' gestation.

- Elizabeth Davies is at 32 weeks' gestation. She telephones for advice. She tells you that her ankles have been very swollen since the previous day. It is Wednesday. The antenatal clinic is held on Mondays.

- Shirley Evans delivered more than 2 weeks ago. Her mother telephones to say that she has just lost a lot of blood, gone pale and had to sit down because she felt faint.

- Susan Foster telephones. She sounds very stressed. She tells you that she is about 7 months pregnant and that she was in contact with her friend's daughter who had a rash. Her friend has just telephoned her to say that her doctor says the girl has German measles. Susan is very upset about the risk to her pregnancy.

In this chapter you have learnt:

■ The range of maternity services that GP's can offer before, during and after the birth.

■ The receptionist's role in maternity care.

■ The importance of certificates such as the FW-8 and Mat-B1.

■ The importance of form FP-24 and how to fill it in.

■ About miscarriages, stillbirths and abortion.

■ Complications that can arise during pregnancy and how your own practice deals with typical problems.

APPENDIX 15a
Form FP-24

Form FP-24 is used by doctors on the FHSA's Obstetric List and form FP-24a is used by doctors not on the Obstetric List. Doctors apply to the FHSA for inclusion on the Obstetric List. Only doctors with obstetric experience will be accepted to the Obstetric List.

Completing the FP-24

The FP-24 is a three-part form:

■ Part I – given to the patient.
■ Part II – the patient's application for maternity services.
■ Part III – the doctor's certificate and claim for payment.

These three parts are explained in more detail below:

Part I

Part I states that the patient is accepted for maternity services, gives the expected date of confinement and is signed by the doctor. It is detached from the main form and given to the patient.

Part II

Part II has four boxes labelled A–D.

When one of your existing patients applies for maternity services you tick *box A*.

When a woman who is already receiving maternity services from another doctor joins your list, you tick *box B* and enter the name and address of the other doctor.

If the woman receives maternity care while temporarily residing in your practice area, you tick *box C*.

If the woman receives emergency maternity care, tick *box D*.

Enter the patient's name, address and date of birth or NHS number in the appropriate spaces.

The date of signing becomes the *date of booking*. The date of booking is used in calculating the fee payable by the FHSA.

Make sure that the patient and the doctor both sign the form.

At the bottom of Part II is the doctor's certificate of *emergency attendance for miscarriage*.

Part III

In the certificate part of the FP-24 you should enter:

■ The patient's name.

■ Her expected date of confinement (EDC).

■ The date of her miscarriage or confinement. (Remember that the date of confinement is the date on which the woman gave birth to her child.)

■ Details of where the birth took place.

The **fee claim part** of the FP-24 is in eight sections, as follows:

Section (i) – tick this box if the GP has provided complete maternity medical services. The GP provides complete maternity medical services if he or she provides ante-natal care, intra-natal care (helps to deliver the baby) (see Section (iv) below) and complete post-natal care.

Section (ii) Ante-natal care – use the obstetric calculator to work out the length of gestation at the date of booking (the day on which she signed the FP-24). Tick one of the boxes (a) (b) or (c) as appropriate. The highest fee for ante-natal care is earned when the FP-24 is signed before 16 weeks' gestation.

Section (iii) – tick this if the pregnancy ended in a miscarriage. If the woman had not yet applied for maternity services, the doctor may sign the special certificate at the bottom of Part II to save distressing the woman by asking her to sign a form for maternity services.

Section (iv) Care during the confinement – if the patient is delivered in a GP hospital or a GP unit attached to a hospital, or has a home delivery, then the GP is deemed to have provided intra-partum care.

Section (v) Complete post-natal care – if the patient was discharged within 48 hours of giving birth (*a 48-hour discharge*), then you should write '48 hr' and the date of discharge in the space provided in this section, and tick the box.

Section (vi) Partial post-natal care – if the doctor did not provide complete post-natal care (Section (v)) then you should enter the dates of up to five post-natal visits in the boxes provided in Section (vi)(a) and tick the box. Enter the date of the post-natal examination in Section (vi)(b).

Section (vii) – in exceptional circumstances the details of the claim may have to be described in an accompanying letter.

Section (viii) – if a patient receiving maternity care leaves the practice before she has had her post-natal examination (the administrative end-point of maternity services), then, as well as entering any pertinent details such as the delivery date (if appropriate) and the dates of any post-natal visits (if appropriate), you should enter the date of last service in Section (viii) and send the form to the FHSA for payment.

Epilogue

Developing Self-sufficiency and Proactivity

Many managers try to encourage proactivity in their staff by asking the question *'And what are you going to do about it?'* of a staff member who has just brought them a problem. A long serving member of staff might simply be asked *'and . . . ?'*.

Generally, avoid answering what you do not know, especially if you have been working in the practice for some time. You might get the response *'Well, that's two of us who do not know, and the practice can only afford one of us'*.

You can stay one step ahead and avoid feeling flummoxed by this question by bringing your seniors *solutions* not *problems*. To do this, when faced with a problem beyond your experience, you obviously outline the issue to your senior, but then you would carry on to say what you had thought of doing to fix it. You then seek an opinion not of the problem but of your solution.

If your manager's solution is different to yours then you could ask why he or she has opted for that particular course.

Use every situation as a learning experience.

Section IV

Appendices

Appendix A

Common Abbreviations in General Practice

ACBS	Advisory Committee on Borderline Substances
AIDS	acquired immune deficiency syndrome
ANC	ante-natal clinic (also ante-natal care)
AN	
ASAP	as soon as possible
BNF	*British National Formulary*
BP	*British Pharmacopoeia* (also blood pressure)
BPAS	British Pregnancy Advisory Service
C&S	culture and sensitivity
CCF	congestive cardiac failure
CCRS	cervical cytology recall system
CD	controlled drug
CNS	central nervous system
CPN	community psychiatric nurse
CXR	chest x-ray
DLA	disabled living allowance
DNA	did not attend
EC	enteric coated
ECG	electro-cardiogram
ECR	extra-contractual referral
EDC	expected date of confinement
EDD	expected date of delivery
EEG	Electro-Encephalogram
EWC	expected week of confinement
FB	foreign body
FHSA	Family Health Services Authority
FPA	Family Planning Association
GA	general anaesthetic
GIT	gastrointestinal tract
GP	General practitioner

Hib	haemophilus influenza b
HIV	human immunodeficiency virus (the cause of AIDS)
IM	intra-muscular
INR	international normalised ratio
IUCD	intra-uterine contraceptive device (coil)
IUD	intra-uterine death (stillbirth); also intra-uterine device (coil) (see also *IUCD*)
IV	intra-venous
LMC	local medical committee
LMP	last menstrual period
MIMS	*Monthly Index of Medical Specialties*
MMR	measles, mumps, rubella (combined vaccine)
MO	medical officer
MRE	medical record envelope ·
MSU	midstream urine (sample)
NAD	nothing abnormal detected
NAI	non-accidental injury
NAR	no action required
NHS	National Health Service
OTC	over-the-counter preparations
OPD	out-patient department
POM	prescription only medicine
PN	post-natal
PPA	Prescription Pricing Authority
R&A	reassured and advised
TCA	to come again
TLC	'tender loving care'
TOP	termination of pregnancy
TR	temporary resident
UTI	urinary tract infection
UWG	usual warnings given
VAC	vaccination session
VI	*vide infra* (Latin) = see below
VS	*vide supra* (Latin) = see above

APPENDIX B

Glossary of Terms

This glossary provides brief and simple explanations of the clinical terminology used in this book. For a fuller explanation we suggest you consult *Baillière's Nursing Dictionary* – see our list of recommended reading for further details.

Acute	A severe pain might be described as *acute*; *acute* may also refer to the first presentation of an illness.
Albuminuria	The presence of albumin, a protein, in urine.
Amphetamine	A frequently abused stimulant drug. Used infrequently as an aid to dieting.
Anaemia	A deficiency of red blood cells or a deficiency of the haemoglobin carried in each red blood cell.
Analgesic	A drug to relieve pain
Antibiotic	A drug to treat infections
Anticoagulant	A drug to slow blood clotting. Used in conditions where the patient's blood is clotting too easily.
Antidepressant	A drug to treat depression
Antihistamine	A drug to treat allergic conditions such as hayfever or urticaria
Antiplatelet	A drug that slows blood clotting. Used in conditions where the patient's blood is clotting too easily.
Arthritis	Inflammation of joints.
Asthma	A disease affecting the lungs characterised by shortness of breath and wheezing.
Barbiturate	A sedating drug. Addictive. Infrequently prescribed nowadays.
Beta blocker	A drug used in many conditions including heart problems, high blood pressure, migraine, and anxiety.
Bronchospasm	A condition resulting in shortness of breath and wheezing. Seen in patients suffering from asthma.
Biochemistry	The study of the various chemicals in blood.
Cervix	The neck of the womb

Cervical smear test	A test to determine whether or not the patient has any pre-malignant or malignant disease in the cervix.
Cocaine	An addictive drug
Chronic	Used to describe a longstanding problem.
Cholecystogram	An x-ray of the gallbladder.
Cancer	A growth or tumour.
Cholesterol	A chemical substance found in the body. High levels of *cholesterol* can be dangerous to health.
Chemoprophylaxis	*Prophylaxis* of disease using chemicals or drugs.
Coeliac disease	A disease of the bowel that results in impaired absorption of food into the body.
Colostomy	An artificial opening into the large bowel (see *stoma*).
Diuretic	A drug that makes the patient pass a greater amount of urine.
Dysentery	A bowel infection that causes severe diarrhoea.
Diabetes	*Diabetes* mellitus is a disease due to an insulin deficiency. The disease may be controlled by diet alone, tablets, or insulin injections.
Diphtheria	An infection. Children are vaccinated against *Diphtheria* in the first year of life.
Epilepsy	A condition of the brain characterised by sudden loss of consciousness with or without violent involuntary jerking of the limbs.
Enema	A fluid introduced into the rectum. Enemata are used to promote bowel movements and in diagnostic x-ray examinations of the lower intestine.
Electroencephalogram (EEG)	A printed tracing of the brain's electrical activity. Electrodes applied around the head detect the electrical currents from the brain.
Electrocardiogram (ECG)	A printed tracing of the heart's electrical activity. The electrical activity is detected by electrodes attached to the patient's limbs and placed across the chest.
Gynaecology	A field of medicine concerned with diseases of women, especially those pertaining to the *genito-urinary* organs.
Genito-urinary	Pertaining to the *genito-urinary* organs.
Glycosuria	The finding of glucose in the urine.
Gestation	The duration of a pregnancy.
Hepatitis	Inflammation of the liver
Hysterectomy	A surgical operation to take away the womb
Haematology	The study of blood cells and the mechanisms of blood clotting.

Hypercholesterolaemia	An abnormally high amount of *cholesterol* in the blood.
Hypothyroidism	An underactive thyroid gland (also known as *myxoedema*).
Haemophilus Influenza B (HiB)	An *organism* capable of causing meningitis.
Haemoglobin	The oxygen carrying part of blood. Haemoglobin gives blood its red colour.
Histology	The study of body tissues. Histology is used to detect abnormalities such as cancerous changes in biopsy samples.
Immunisation	Protection against infection.
Influenza	An infection affecting the respiratory tract.
Intrauterine contraceptive device	A contraceptive device inserted into the womb.
Inflammation	A bodily reaction to infection or injury characterised by heat, redness, swelling and pain.
Jaundice	A yellowing of the skin and the eyes due to a problem with the liver.
Mumps	An infection characterised by swelling of glands.
Meningitis	An infection around the brain.
Measles	A childhood illness with a characteristic rash.
Microbiology	The identification and control of the bacteria and viruses that cause infection in humans.
Myxoedema	See *hypothyroidism*.
Narcotic	A drug that can induce numbness and stupor. Narcotic *analgesics* are commonly used in medicine. Narcotic drugs are also commonly abused. They are highly addictive.
Oesophagus	That part of the alimentary canal between the throat and the stomach. Also sometimes called the gullet.
Organism	Any living animal or plant. Used by doctors to refer to bacteria and viruses.
Ophthalmia neonatorum	An eye infection in the newborn.
Photo-sensitivity	Undue sensitivity of the skin to sunshine.
Pathology	The study of body tissues altered by disease.
Phlebotomist	A person who takes blood samples.
Poliomyelitis	An infection causing paralysis.
Pertussis	An infection. Also known as Whooping Cough.

Pre-malignant changes	Changes suggestive of cancer but not yet cancerous. Generally a treatable phase of the illness.
Progesterone	A female hormone.
Prophylaxis	Prevention of disease.
Rubella	An infection. Its only importance is in pregnancy.
Radio-opaque	Does not allow x-rays to pass through. Bones are largely radio-opaque. Radio-opaque dyes can be used to facilitate x-ray examination of otherwise non-radio-opaque organs such as the gallbladder or the kidneys.
Serum	A part of blood
Suture (verb)	To stitch a cut or wound.
Stoma	An opening into the body for drainage or other purposes. A patient who has had a colostomy would have a stoma.
Scarlet fever	An infection associated with a rash. Scarletina is a minor form of the infection.
Tetanus	A type of infection (also known as lockjaw).
Thyroid	A gland in the front of the neck.
Uterus	The womb.
Vaccination	Protection against infection.
Virus	An organism. Many viruses have the potential to cause disease in Man.

APPENDIX C

Useful Addresses

Association of Medical Secretaries Practice Administrators and Receptionists Ltd (AMSPAR).

> Tavistock House North
> Tavistock Square
> LONDON WC1H 9LN
>
> Tel: 0171-387-6005
> Fax: 0171-388-2648

AMSPAR run courses for medical secretaries and receptionists and, amongst other qualifications, award a Certificate in General Practice Reception.

A useful directory of self-help and support organisations entitled 'The Health Address Book' is available from:

> The Patients Association
> 18, Victoria Park Square
> Bethnal Green
> London E2 9PF
>
> Tel: 0181-981-5676

APPENDIX D
Further Reading and Resources

PRACTICE MANAGEMENT

'The Practice Receptionist Programme' is a modular training programme produced and organised by:

The Radcliffe Medical Press Ltd
18, Marcham Road
Abingdon
OX14 1AA

Tel: 01235 528820
Fax: 01235 528830

The programme is designed to be used in conjunction with locally arranged tutorial groups.

DRURY M and HOLDEN-CLARK L (1993) The Practice Manager, Oxford. Radcliffe Medical Press.

Deals with the managerial issues of general practice. Useful further reading if you want to advance your career in practice management.

JONE R J N, BOLDEN K J, PEREIRA GRAY D J, HALL M S (1990) Running a Practice – a manual of Practice Management. London. Chapman and Hall.

Aimed at doctors in general practice but gives a good introduction to the wider issues of general practice management.

We also suggest that you read the practice management and finance sections in the following magazines:

GP, Pulse (and Pulse finance), Doctor and Medeconomics.

These magazines are sent to most GPs' surgeries and also contain a lot of news about General Practice matters.

CLINICAL/MEDICAL TERMINOLOGY

WELLER B F and WELLS R J (1990) Baillière's Nursing Dictionary. London. Baillière-Tindall.

A useful and comprehensive guide – you may find that your practice already has one.

INTERPERSONAL SKILLS

LINDENFIELD G (1986) Assert Yourself. London. Thorsons.

A concise introduction to assertiveness skills with a useful section on dealing with complaints.

ALLEN J (1993) How to solve your people problems. London. Kogan Page.

Although aimed at supervisory staff this book gives a good introduction to inter-personal skills in plain language.

MYSERSCOUGH P R (1992) Talking with Patients – A basic clinical skill. Oxford. Oxford University Press.

Directed at doctors but contains useful example dialogues. Clear and easy to read.

COMPUTING

GOOKIN D and RATHBONE A (1995) PCs for dummies. California. IDG.

A classic example of a book 'for the rest of us'. Here you will find computers explained clearly for non-technical people.

(1995) Computers Simplified. The 3D visual approach. California. IDG.

This is another excellent introduction to computers, but at a much higher price than 'PCs for dummies'. This book features superb 3D effect graphics which clearly explain all the basics including modems, printers, and networks.

INDEX

NOTES

NOTES

NOTES

NOTES

NOTES

NOTES

NOTES

NOTES